SOLID MENSURATION

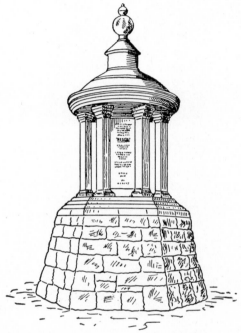

GENERAL GEORGE E. PICKETT'S MONUMENT, HOLLYWOOD CEMETERY, RICHMOND, VIRGINIA

This monument embodies, in general, all the solids considered in "Solid Mensuration."

SOLID MENSURATION
WITH PROOFS

BY
WILLIS F. KERN

Associate Professor of Mathematics, Retired,
U. S. Naval Academy

AND

JAMES R. BLAND

Professor of Mathematics, Retired,
U. S. Naval Academy

SECOND EDITION

NEW YORK
JOHN WILEY & SONS, Inc.
LONDON: CHAPMAN & HALL, LIMITED

PREFACE TO SECOND EDITION

The purpose of Solid Mensuration is to present the fundamental, practical essentials of solid geometry in a new and concise but comprehensive manner. To accomplish this purpose more completely the authors have entirely rewritten the original text.

One of the most important objects to be gained by a study of solid geometry is the development of a space intuition. To attain this object we have introduced a large number of exercises which call for visualization of cross sections of solids in connection with reducing a problem in solid geometry to a number of simple problems in plane geometry.

Perhaps the most distinctive feature of this revision is the inclusion of simple proofs of the volume and surface formulas. These proofs appeal to the intuition. The conventional treatment has been simplified by basing the proof of each volume formula on Cavalieri's Theorem. A considerable simplification is obtained by considering first the elementary and most familiar solids and by separating the solids into natural groups. The treatment of the solids for which $V = Bh$ is in the first group, the solids for which $V = \frac{1}{3}Bh$ is in the second group, and the solids for which $V = (\text{mean } B)h$ is in the third group.

Most of the problems and illustrative examples relate to familiar objects of everyday experience. Many of the problems require thought and visualization. Each has been carefully selected with the thought of stimulating the student's imagination and developing his space intuition.

Four-place tables of logarithms, of natural trigonometric functions, and of logarithms of trigonometric functions have been included. A number of new and distinctive features connected with the table of logarithms give a gain in simplicity, speed, and accuracy.

The labor of the authors will be amply repaid if this revised edition meets with the generous favor accorded Solid Mensuration since its first appearance.

ACKNOWLEDGMENTS

The authors take pleasure in expressing their appreciation of the help given by the members of the Department of Mathematics at the United States Naval Academy. Captains W. W. Smith, H. K. Hewitt, and L. B. McBride rendered helpful assistance. Professors Paul Capron, Charles L. Leiper, James B. Eppes, Levi T. Wilson, Dr. N. Hansen Ball, and Dr. Sebastian B. Littauer have contributed valuable ideas and problems. Professor James B. Scarborough has critically read the manuscript throughout and given many contributions and much constructive criticism. Professor Lyman M. Kells has suggested many changes in the manuscript which have added greatly to its value. Professor John Tyler supplied the material for the chapter on the general prismatoid.

WILLIS F. KERN
JAMES R. BLAND

ANNAPOLIS, MD.
May, 1938

CONTENTS

APPENDIX

TABLES

SOLID MENSURATION

CHAPTER I

PLANE FIGURES

1. INTRODUCTION

Solid Mensuration deals primarily with the various solids. The formulas developed in this text are used extensively in railway engineering, in road and bridge construction, in chemical and physical analyses, and in a large variety of commercial and engineering projects. As we study Solid Mensuration we shall see how necessary it is to have a thorough knowledge of the mensuration of solids.

2. COMPUTATION SUGGESTIONS

When solving a problem in Solid Mensuration, draw an appropriate figure on which all dimensions are shown. Write down all formulas by means of which the unknown quantities are to be found. Be sure that your work is arranged so that it can be followed at any time by yourself or another person. A study of the examples solved in the text will aid the student in making adequate arrangements for himself. In many problems it is helpful to employ literal quantities to denote numerical values in carrying on the work. However, in completing a problem it is necessary finally to replace these literal quantities by the numbers they represent.

Logarithms. A four-place table of logarithms is given on p. 156. This table is unique in that it includes special tables of proportional parts together with tabular differences. The simplicity of operation resulting from these features permits both greater speed and greater accuracy.

Slide Rule. The use of a slide rule in connection with a course in Solid Mensuration, besides showing the power and limitations of the instrument, enlivens the course considerably. It interests the student to find, after spending considerable time in the computation of a problem, that he can use his slide rule to obtain a result usually accurate to three figures in a fraction of the time.

There are many types of slide rules available. The " L L Trig Duplex* Slide Rule " and the " Polyphase Trig Duplex* Slide Rule " are two of the best and are especially suited for use when performing computations in connection with the solution of engineering problems. A manual of explanation accompanies each of these slide rules. This manual has been written for study without the aid of a teacher. The subject matter is so presented that the beginner uses two general principles while he is learning to read the scales and perform the simpler operations. The mastery of these two principles gives the power to devise the best settings for any particular purpose, and to recall settings that have been forgotten.

Trigonometry. Included in each list of problems are some which require the use of trigonometry in their solution. These are indicated by the symbol ★.

A four-place table of logarithms of the trigonometric functions and a four-place table of natural trigonometric functions are given on pp. 156–159.

3. MENSURATION OF PLANE FIGURES

A large part of the work of this textbook has to do with the computation of surface areas and the volumes of solids. In this connection it is frequently necessary to pass a plane through a solid to form a plane section, find the area of this section, and multiply it by the length of a line. Thus it is important for the student to be thoroughly familiar with the mensuration of the standard plane figures. For this reason he should carefully review the following list of formulas relating to plane figures.

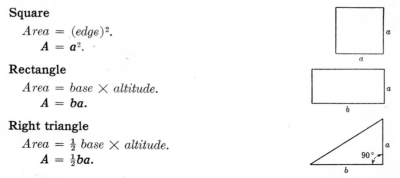

Square

$$Area = (edge)^2.$$
$$A = a^2.$$

Rectangle

$$Area = base \times altitude.$$
$$A = ba.$$

Right triangle

$$Area = \tfrac{1}{2}\,base \times altitude.$$
$$A = \tfrac{1}{2}ba.$$

* Registered U. S. Pat. Off. by Keuffel and Esser Co., Hoboken, N. J.

Pythagorean theorem.

(Hypotenuse)² = sum of the squares of the two legs.

$$c^2 = a^2 + b^2, \quad \text{or} \quad a = \sqrt{(c - b)(c + b)}.$$

Special right triangles

  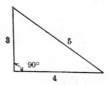

Some other right triangles, the measures of whose sides are all whole numbers which satisfy the Pythagorean theorem, are: 5–12–13; 7–24–25; 8–15–17; 20–21–29; 16–63–65; 13–84–85; 119–120–169.

Oblique triangle

Area = ½ base × altitude.
$$A = \tfrac{1}{2}bh.$$

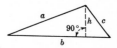

$$A = \sqrt{s(s - a)(s - b)(s - c)}, \quad \text{where } s = \frac{(a + b + c)}{2}.$$

Parallelogram (opposite sides parallel)

Area = base × altitude.
$$A = bh.$$

Trapezoid (one pair of opposite sides parallel)

Area = ½ sum of bases × altitude.
$$A = \tfrac{1}{2}(a + b)h.$$

Circle

Circumference = 2π(radius) = π(diameter).
$$C = 2\pi R = \pi D.$$

Area = π(radius)² = $\dfrac{\pi}{4}$ (diameter)².

$$A = \pi R^2 = \frac{\pi}{4}D^2.$$

Sector of circle

Area = ½ radius × arc.
$$A = \tfrac{1}{2}Rc = \tfrac{1}{2}R^2\theta.$$

Segment of circle

$$Area_{(segment)} = Area_{(sector)} - Area_{(triangle)}$$
$$A = \tfrac{1}{2}Rc - \tfrac{1}{2}ba.$$

Ellipse

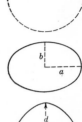

$$Area = \pi ab.$$

Parabolic segment.

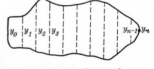

$$Area = \tfrac{2}{3}ld.$$

Area by approximation

The area of any irregular plane figure (such as the one shown) can be found approximately by dividing it into an *even* number of strips or panels by a series of equidistant parallel chords y_0, y_1, y_2, ..., y_n, the com-
mon distance between the chords being
h.   The required area is then given by the following formula

$$A = \frac{h}{3}(y_0 + 4y_1 + 2y_2 + \ldots + 2y_{n-2} + 4y_{n-1} + y_n).$$

The larger the value of n, in general the greater is the accuracy of approximation.

Similar figures

Similar polygons are polygons that have their homologous angles equal and their homologous sides proportional.   In general, *corre-*
sponding lines of similar figures are in the
same ratio.   Similar polygons have the same
ratio as the squares of any two corresponding
lines.

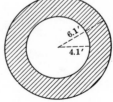

Example 1.   The section (see figure) of a cer-
tain solid is bounded by two concentric circles whose radii are 6.1 ft. and 4.1 ft.   Find the area of this section.

Solution.   Let A_l and A_s denote the areas of the larger and smaller circles, respectively. Using the formula for the area of a circle, we have

$$A_l = \pi (6.1)^2$$

and

$$A_s = \pi (4.1)^2.$$

Since the difference between these two areas is the area of the section, we write

$$A_l - A_s = \pi (6.1)^2 - \pi (4.1)^2 = \pi [(6.1)^2 - (4.1)^2]$$
$$= \pi (6.1 + 4.1)\ (6.1 - 4.1)$$
$$= \pi (10.2)\ (2) = \textbf{64.089 sq. ft.}\quad Ans.$$

Example 2. The section of a certain solid consists of a semicircle, a rectangle, and a triangle, as shown. The altitude of the rectangle is three times the radius of the semicircle, the altitude of the triangle is twice the same radius, and the area of the triangle is 20 sq. ft. Find the area of the section.

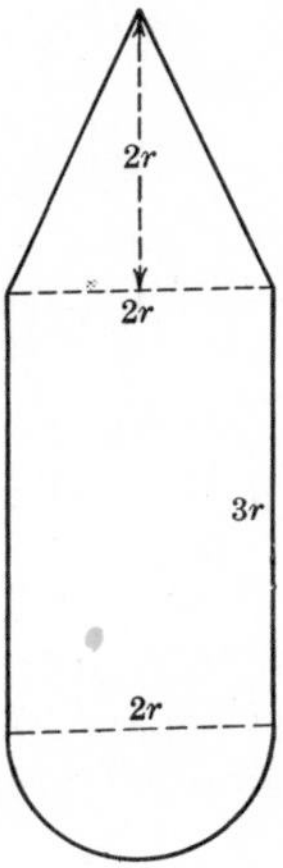

Solution. Let A_t, A_r, and A_c denote the areas of the triangle, rectangle, and semicircle, respectively. Using formulas listed in this article under the appropriate headings, we find in terms of r

$$A_t = \tfrac{1}{2}(2r)\ (2r) = 2r^2,$$
$$A_r = (2r)\ (3r) = 6r^2,$$
$$A_c = \tfrac{1}{2}\pi r^2.$$

Since the area of the section A is the sum of these areas, we have

$$A = A_t + A_r + A_c = 2r^2 + 6r^2 + \tfrac{1}{2}\pi r^2 = \frac{r^2}{2}\ (16 + \pi).\quad (a)$$

Equating the area of the triangle in terms of r to its given area, we get

$$20 = \tfrac{1}{2}(2r)\ (2r).$$

Solving this equation for r^2, we obtain

$$r^2 = 10.$$

Substituting this value of r^2 in equation (a), we get

$$A = \tfrac{10}{2}(16 + \pi) = \textbf{95.708 sq. ft.}\quad Ans.$$

Example 3. A city block is in the form of a parallelogram whose shorter diagonal AB is perpendicular to side BC, as shown in the figure. The shorter sides represent streets and the longer sides repre-

sent avenues.   If the distance between the avenues is 400 ft. and the
length of each street is 500 ft., find the area of the block.

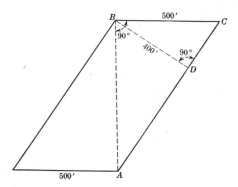

Solution.   From B drop the perpendicular BD to line AC.   Since
BD by construction is the distance between the avenues,

$$BD = 400.$$

Applying the Pythagorean theorem to right triangle BDC, we obtain

$$DC = \sqrt{(500)^2 - (400)^2} = 300.$$

Since the sides of angle DBC are respectively perpendicular to the sides
of angle BAC, angle DBC = angle BAC.   Hence right triangles DBC
and BAC are similar.   Consequently, we write

$$\frac{AB}{500} = \frac{400}{300}.$$

Solving for AB, we get

$$AB = \frac{2000}{3}.$$

Considering BC as base and AB as altitude of the parallelogram, we
have for its area

$$(BC)\,(AB) = (500)\left(\frac{2000}{3}\right) \text{ sq. ft.} = \left(\frac{500}{9}\right)\left(\frac{2000}{3}\right) \text{ sq. yd.} =$$
$$\textbf{37,037 sq. yd.}\quad Ans.$$

PROBLEMS

1. A window glass is 4 ft. 2 in. by 2 ft. 10 in.   Find its area.

2. Find the area of the largest circle which can be cut from a square of
edge 4 in.   What is the area of the material wasted?

3. A garden plot is to contain 200 sq. ft. If its length is to be twice its width, what should its dimensions be?

4. Find the length of the diagonal of: (a) a square in terms of its edge a; (b) a rectangle in terms of its base b and its altitude h.

5. Find the area of an equilateral triangle of side a.

6. Express the area of a circle in terms of the diameter d.

7. Write a formula for the circumference of a circle in terms of the diameter d.

8. The official distance between home plate and second base in a baseball diamond is 120 ft. Find the area of the official ball diamond and the distances between the bases. (The official ball diamond is in the form of a square.)

9. A metal washer 1 in. in diameter is pierced by a $\frac{1}{2}$-in. hole. What is the area of one face of the washer?

10. A certain city block is in the form of a parallelogram. Two of its sides are each 421 ft. long; the other two sides are each 227 ft. in length. If the distance between the first pair of sides is 126 ft., find the area of the land in the block, and the length of the diagonals.

11. The vertical end of a trough has the following dimensions: width at top 4.4 ft., width at bottom 3.2 ft., depth 3.5 ft. Find the area of the end of the trough.

12. A sail has a spread of canvas as shown in the figure. Find the surface area of one side of the sail.

13. A storage bin of circular base has 324 sq. ft. of floor space. Find the radius of the floor.

14. The plane area shown in the figure consists of an isosceles trapezoid (non-parallel sides equal) and a segment of a circle. If the non-parallel sides are tangent to the segment at points A and B, find the area of the composite figure.

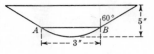

15. Find the area of the rectilinear figure shown, if it is the difference between two isosceles trapezoids whose corresponding sides are parallel.

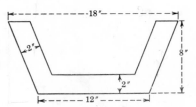

16. The points C and D in the figure lie on level ground in the same vertical plane with the tip B of the tower AB. If the tower AB is 300 ft. high and measurements give $A_1B_1 = 5$ ft., $CA_1 = 12$ ft., $A_2B_2 = 6$ ft., and $A_2D = 8$ ft., find the distance CD.

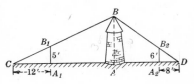

17. The quarter-mile race track shown in the figure has parallel sides AB and CD, each 315 ft. long. If the ends are semicircles, find the area

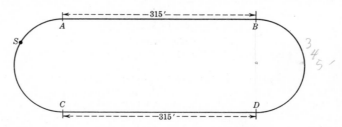

bounded by the track. If a race is run from S to D by way of C, find the length of the race in yards, given that arc $SC = \frac{44}{47} \times$ arc AC. (1 mile = 5280 ft.)

18. Each of the four circles shown in the figure is tangent to the other three. (*a*) If the radius of each of the smaller circles is a, find the area of the largest circle. (*b*) If $a = 2.71$ what is the area of the largest circle?

19. The base of an isosceles triangle is 16 in. and the altitude is 15 in. Find the radius of the inscribed circle.

★20. In the figure of Prob. 14 change the angle from 60° to 41° and then solve the problem.

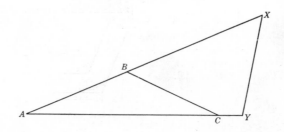

21. Show that, for the two triangles ABC and AXY (see figure),

$$\frac{\text{Area of } ABC}{\text{Area of } AXY} = \frac{AB \times AC}{AX \times AY}.$$

CHAPTER II

LINES — PLANES — ANGLES

4. LINES AND PLANES IN SPACE

Def. 1. A *plane* is a surface such that a straight line joining any two points in it lies wholly in the surface. A plane is understood to be indefinite in extent, but is usually represented by a parallelogram lying in the plane. (See figure.)

Solid geometry or geometry of space treats primarily of figures all of whose elements do not lie in the same plane.

Axiom A. A finite number of planes do not contain all points in space.

Postulate 1. Through three points not in the same straight line, one and only one plane can be passed.

Postulate 2. If two planes meet they have at least two distinct points in common.

Def. 2. Two *parallel lines* are lines that lie in the same plane and cannot meet however far they are produced.

Def. 3. Two *planes* which do not intersect however far produced are said to be *parallel*.

Def. 4. A *straight line* and a *plane* are *parallel* if they cannot meet, however far both are produced.

A complete theory of solid geometry can be based on the axioms and theorems of plane geometry (see Appendix, §50) together with the axiom, postulates, and definitions just given. The following definitions and theorems are fundamental in Solid Mensuration.

Def. 5. When we suppose a plane to be drawn through given points or lines, we are said to *pass* the plane through the given points or lines.

Def. 6. When a straight line is drawn from a point to a plane, its intersection with the plane is called its *foot*.

9

Def. 7. A straight line and a plane are *perpendicular* if the line is perpendicular to every straight line drawn through its foot in the plane. A perpendicular to a plane is often referred to as a *normal* to the plane.

Def. 8. The *projection of a point* on a plane is the foot of the perpendicular let fall from the point to the plane.

Def. 9. The *projection of a line* on a plane is the locus of the projections of all its points.

Def. 10. The *angle* which *a line makes with a plane* is the angle which it makes with its projection on the plane.

Theorems

1. *If two planes intersect, their intersection is a straight line.*

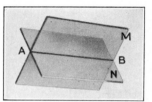

Thus if planes *M* and *N* (see figure) intersect, their intersection *AB* is a straight line.

2. *A plane is determined (a) by a straight line and a point without that line, (b) by two intersecting straight lines, (c) by two parallel lines.*

3. *Through one straight line any number of planes may be passed.*

4. *The intersections of two parallel planes by a third plane are parallel lines.* Thus in the case of the two parallel planes *M* and *N* cut by plane *L*, the intersections *a* and *b* are parallel lines.

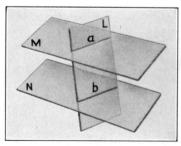
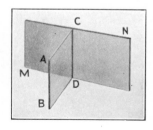

5. *If two straight lines are parallel, a plane containing one, and only one, is parallel to the other line.* Thus in the figure if the two straight lines *AB* and *CD* are parallel and if plane *MN* contains *CD* it is parallel to *AB*.

6. *If a straight line is parallel to a plane, and another plane containing this line intersects the given plane, the intersection is parallel to the given line.* Thus if line AB (see figure) is parallel to plane MN, and if plane AD containing AB intersects MN, the intersection CD is parallel to AB.

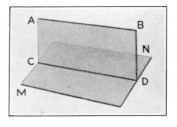

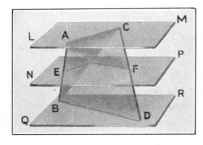

7. *If parallel planes intersect two straight lines, the corresponding intercepts are proportional.* Thus if the parallel planes LM, NP, and QR (see figure) intersect lines AB and CD, then

$$\frac{AE}{EB} = \frac{CF}{FD}.$$

8. *Two straight lines that are parallel to a third straight line are parallel to each other.* Thus if lines CD and EF (see figure) are each parallel to line AB, then CD is parallel to EF.

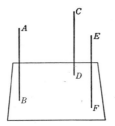

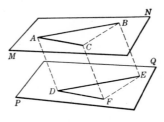

9. *If two angles, not in the same plane, have their sides parallel each to each, and extending in the same directions from their vertices, the angles are equal and the planes are parallel.* Thus angle BAC in plane MN is equal to angle EDF in plane PQ and MN is parallel to PQ, if side AB is parallel to side DE and if side AC is parallel to side DF.

10. *A straight line perpendicular to each of two straight lines at their intersection is perpendicular to the plane of the lines.* Thus if

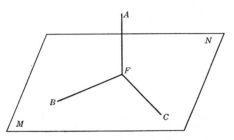

line *AF* is perpendicular to lines *BF* and *CF* in the plane *MN* (see figure), *AF* is perpendicular to any other line in *MN* through *F* and

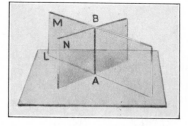

so is perpendicular to the plane *MN*.

11. *If two planes are perpendicular to a third plane, their intersection also is perpendicular to that plane.* Thus in the case of the two planes *M* and *N* which are perpendicular to a third plane *L* their intersection *AB* is perpendicular to plane *L*.

12. *All the perpendiculars that can be drawn to a straight line at a given point lie in a plane which is perpendicular to the line at the given point* (see figure).

13. *If one of two parallel lines is perpendicular to a plane, the other is also.*

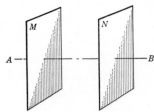

14. *Two straight lines perpendicular to the same plane are parallel.*

15. *Two planes perpendicular to the same straight line are parallel.* Thus if planes *M* and *N* (see figure) are each perpendicular to line *AB*, they are parallel.

16. *A straight line perpendicular to one of two parallel planes is perpendicular to the other also.*

5. TYPICAL PROOFS OF SOLID GEOMETRY

We shall now demonstrate two of these theorems to illustrate the type of proof met in solid geometry.

3. *Through one straight line any number of planes may be passed.*

Analysis. Let AB in the figure be a straight line. By Axiom A there is a point outside AB. By Theorem 2 this point together with the line determines a plane. By Axiom A there is a point

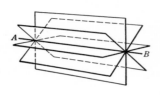
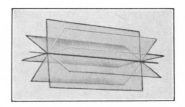

outside this plane. This point together with the given line determine a second plane. By Axiom A there is a point outside these two planes. This point together with line AB determine a third plane. The proof applied to establish the existence of each of these three planes may be repeated indefinitely to show that any number of planes may be passed through the line AB.

10. *A straight line perpendicular to each of two straight lines at their intersection is perpendicular to the plane of the lines.*

Analysis. Given line AF perpendicular to lines BF and CF at F; plane MN containing BF and CF. In plane MN draw BC; draw also DF from F to any point D in BC. Prolong AF to X, making $FX = AF$, and draw AB, AD, AC, BX, DX, CX.

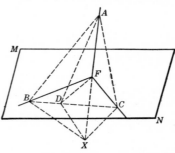

BF and CF are perpendicular bisectors of AX (Hyp. and Const.)

In $\triangle ABC$ and BXC, $AB = BX$ and $AC = CX$,   (51)*

$$BC = BC. \qquad (?)$$

Therefore $\triangle ABC \cong \triangle BXC.$ (35)

* These references refer to " References from Plane Geometry," Appendix, § 50.

Also in △ ABD and BXD, angle ABC = angle CBX,   (46)

$$BD = BD,$$ (?)

and $$AB = BX.$$ (?)

Therefore $$\triangle ABD \cong \triangle BXD.$$ (34)

Therefore $$AD = DX.$$ (?)

Hence DF is perpendicular to AX.   (52)

That is,

AF is perpendicular to all lines in MN through F.

Therefore

AF is perpendicular to plane MN.   (Def. 7)

EXERCISES

1. How many planes can be passed through two points? Through three points in the same straight line?

2. Do any two planes intersect? Explain.

3. Hold a piece of chalk parallel to the blackboard, so that its shadow falls on the blackboard. Is this shadow parallel to the chalk? Why?

4. If two lines are perpendicular to a third line are they necessarily in the same plane? Are the two lines necessarily parallel? Why?

5. When will a line on the ceiling be parallel to a line on the floor?

6. What information can the mason or the surveyor obtain from a plumb bob? Does he obtain this information when the bob is swinging or when it is at rest?

7. Considered as lines, why are the spokes of a wagon wheel perpendicular to the axle?

8. How many planes are determined by four fixed points not all in one plane?

9. If three lines are perpendicular to the same plane are they necessarily parallel?

10. Find the length of the projection of a 5-ft. rod, inclined at an angle of (a) 60°; (b) 30°; (c) 45°; ★(d) 37°; ★(e) 42° 15′.

11. Four points in space A, B, C, D, are joined by four lines which are then bisected. Show that the four lines joining (in order) the four midpoints of the first lines form a parallelogram.

Hint. Pass plane DP (see figure) through points A, D, B, and plane DX through points B, C, D — these planes intersecting in BD. ST is parallel to BD and = $\frac{1}{2}BD$.

12. A street light is 15 ft. directly above the curb. A man 6 ft. tall starts 10 ft. down street from the light and walks directly across the street which is 10 ft. wide. When he reaches the opposite curb, what is the distance between the initial and final positions of the tip of his shadow?

6. ANGLES

Def. 11. A *dihedral angle* is the amount of divergence of two intersecting planes. The *edge* of the dihedral angle is the line of intersection of the planes. The *faces* of the dihedral angle are the planes. The intersecting planes *AG* and *ED* form the dihedral angle whose edge is *EG*, which is designated *A–GE–D*; or, when there is only one dihedral angle at the edge, " the angle *EG*."

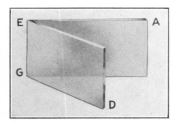 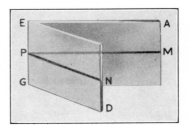

Def. 12. The *plane angle* of a dihedral angle is the angle formed by two straight lines, one in each face, and perpendicular to the edge at the same point. If *PM* is in plane *AG* and perpendicular to *EG*, and *PN* is in plane *ED* and perpendicular to *EG* at *P*, the angle *MPN* is the plane angle of the dihedral angle *EG*.

17. *The plane angle of a dihedral angle is taken as the measure of the dihedral angle.* 2 faced ∠s

Def. 13. Two *planes* are *perpendicular* to each other if they form a dihedral angle whose plane angle is a right angle.

18. *Every point in a plane bisecting a dihedral angle is equally distant from the faces of the angle* (see figure).

Def. 14. If three or more planes meet at a point, they form a *polyhedral angle*. The opening partially surrounded by the planes is the polyhedral angle. The point common to all the

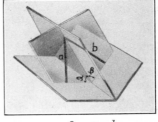

$$\alpha = \beta, \quad a = b$$

planes is the *vertex*. The planes are the *faces*. The intersections of adjacent faces are the *edges*. The angles formed at the vertex, by adjacent edges, are the *face angles*. The angles made by the planes, at the edges, are the *dihedrals* of the *polyhedral*.

Thus, $V-ABCDE$ is a polyhedral angle; V is the vertex; AV, BV, etc., are edges; planes LVM, MVN, etc., are faces; angles AVB, BVC, etc., are face angles.

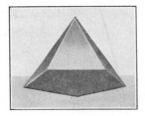
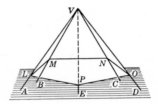

EXERCISES

1. Show that the angle between the normals drawn to the faces of a dihedral angle from a point within the angle is the supplement of the plane angle of the dihedral angle.

2. Show that, if, from any point P in a face of a dihedral angle (see figure), a normal is drawn to each face, the plane PAB of these normals is perpendicular to the edge of the dihedral angle ON.

3. Show that if from any point P in a face of a dihedral angle (see figure) a normal is drawn to each face, the angle APB between these normals is equal to the plane angle ACP of the dihedral angle.

GENERAL EXERCISES

1. How can two pencils (representing lines) be held so that a plane can be passed containing both; so that no plane can be passed containing both?

2. What is meant by the statement, "Two planes determine a line"? Is this universally true?

3. Can a plane intersect two planes that are not parallel so that the intersections are parallel? Illustrate your answer by passing a plane through the edges of an open book. How must this plane be passed so that the intersections are parallel lines?

4. If two lines do not intersect, can a third line be drawn perpendicular to them?

5. Why are the corner edges of a building perpendicular to the plane of a level street?

6. How many positions can a lightning rod erected at a point occupy without being vertical? How many positions may it assume and be vertical?

7. In erecting a vertical column a carpenter may use a carpenter's square to make certain that the column is perpendicular to the floor. In how many different positions must he place the square against the column to ascertain whether it is vertical? Why?

8. Can a line be perpendicular to both of two planes if they are not parallel?

9. Can one line be perpendicular to two other lines that intersect?   Explain.

10. A pole 26 ft. long leans against a wall at a point 10 ft. from the ground.   What is the length of the projection of the pole on the ground?

11. Show that if, from the foot of a perpendicular to a plane, a line is drawn normal to any line in the plane, the line connecting this point of intersection with any point in the perpendicular is normal to the line in the plane.

Hint. Draw AB perpendicular to plane RS, BC perpendicular to DE in the plane, and PC from C to P, in AB.   Take $CD = CE$; draw PD, PE, BD, BE.

CHAPTER III

SOLIDS FOR WHICH $V = Bh$

7. INTRODUCTION

In this chapter we discuss certain solids, develop formulas for finding their volumes and surface areas, and apply these formulas in the solution of various practical problems. In general, the student will use but a single new formula in the mensuration of the volumes of these solids.

8. SOLIDS — SECTIONS

A *solid* is any limited portion of space, bounded by surfaces.

A *section* of a solid is the plane figure cut from the solid by pass-

 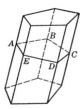

ing a plane through it. Thus, in the case of the solid shown, plane M cuts from the solid the section $ABCDE$.

A polyhedron is a solid bounded by planes.

The *edges* of a polyhedron are the intersections of the bounding planes.

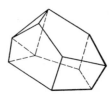

The *faces* are the portions of the bounding planes included by the edges. The faces are polygons.

The *vertices* are the intersections of the edges

9. CUBE

Definition. *A cube is a polyhedron whose six faces are all squares.*

Properties

1. The three dimensions of a cube are equal to each other. Therefore, all edges are equal.

2. All the faces of a cube are congruent squares.

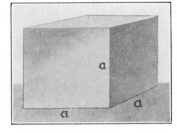

Formulas

The total area of a cube is equal to the sum of the areas of its faces.

Total area = 6 (*area of one face*).

$$T = 6a^2.$$

The volume of a cube is equal to the cube of its edge.

$$Volume = (edge)^3.$$
$$V = a^3.$$

Surface analysis. Each of the six faces of a cube is a square of edge a. Since the area of one face is a^2, the total area of the cube is $6a^2$.

Volume analysis. *The volume of a solid is the number of times it contains a given solid which is chosen arbitrarily as the unit of volume.* A cube whose edge is a linear unit, as one inch or one foot, will be taken as the unit of volume. We shall assume that the volume of a cube is the product of its three dimensions. Hence the volume of a cube of edge a is a^3.

Example 1. A glass factory has an order for 1000 glass paper weights. Each is to be in the form of a cube. If this order requires 8000 cu. in. of glass, what is the surface area of one of the paper weights?

Solution. Let V be the volume of one of the cubes. Then

$$1000V = 8000, \quad \text{or} \quad V = 8. \tag{a}$$

But in terms of an edge a

$$V = a^3. \tag{b}$$

Equating the values of V from equations (a) and (b), we obtain

$$a^3 = 8, \quad \text{or} \quad a = 2,$$

whence

$$T = 6a^2 = 6(2)^2 = \textbf{24 sq. in.} \quad Ans.$$

Example 2. A cube of edge a is cut by a plane containing two diagonally opposite edges of the cube. Find the area of the section thus formed.

Solution. Through the cube pass a plane containing edges AD and BC, forming the section $ABCD$ shown in the figure. Consider AB as base of $ABCD$ and BC as altitude. Applying the Pythagorean theorem to right triangle AEB, we have

$$AB = \sqrt{a^2 + a^2} = a\sqrt{2}.$$

The area of rectangle $ABCD$ is

$$AB \times BC = (a\sqrt{2})\,(a) = a^2\sqrt{2}. \quad Ans.$$

PROBLEMS

1. Find the length of the diagonal of the section $ABCD$ (diagonal of the cube) in Ex. 2.

2. How much material was used in the manufacture of 24,000 celluloid dice, if each die has an edge of $\frac{1}{4}$ in.?

3. Plato (429–348 b.c.) was one of the first to discover a solution to that famous problem of antiquity, the duplication of a cube, i.e., the finding of the edge of a cube whose volume is double that of a given cube.

One legend asserts that the Athenians, who were suffering from a plague of typhoid fever, consulted the oracle at Delos as to how to stop the plague. Apollo replied that the Delians would have to double the size of his altar, which was in the form of a cube. A new altar was constructed having its edge twice as long as that of the old one. But the pestilence became worse than before, whereupon the Delians appealed to Plato. Given that the side of the altar was 8 ft., find, accurate to five figures, the edge of the required altar.

4. Show that (a) the total surface of a cube is twice the square of its diagonal, (b) the volume of a cube is $\frac{1}{9}\sqrt{3}$ times the cube of its diagonal.

5. What is the weight of a block of ice 24 in. by 24 in. by 24 in., if ice weighs 92 per cent as much as water, and water weighs 62.5 lb. per cu. ft.?

6. Find the volume and total area of the largest cube of wood that can be cut from a log of circular cross section whose radius is 12.7 in.   (See sketch.)

7. A vegetable bin built in the form of a cube with an edge of 6 ft. is divided by a vertical partition which passes through two diagonally opposite edges. Find the lateral surface of either compartment.

8. Imagine a cube measuring 3 units on an edge, and having its total surface area painted blue. Without the aid of a figure, answer the following questions.

(A) How many times must you cut completely through the cube to make cubes which measure 1 unit on an edge?

(*B*) How many of the cubes of question (*A*) will have
   (*a*) Three blue faces?
   (*b*) Two blue faces?
   (*c*) One blue face?
   (*d*) No blue face?
(*C*) How many cubes are there in all?
(*D*) How many times must you cut completely through one of the cubes
of (*a*) to make cubes which measure ½ unit on an edge?
(*E*) Answer questions (*B*) and (*C*) with reference to the cubes of (*D*).

   9. The plane section *ABCD* shown in the figure is cut from a cube of edge *a*.
Find the area of this section if *D* and *C* are each
at the midpoint of an edge.

   10. Find the area of a triangle whose vertex
is at the midpoint of an upper edge of a cube
of edge *a* and whose base coincides with the
diagonally opposite edge of the cube.

   11. If a cube has an edge equal to the diagonal of another cube, find the ratio of their
volumes.

   12. One cube has a face equivalent to the
total area of another cube. Find the ratio of
their volumes.

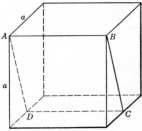

   13. Pass a plane through a cube so that the section formed will be a regular
hexagon. If the edge of the cube is 2 units, find the area of this section.

   ★**14.** In Prob. 9 find the angle which the section *ABCD* makes with the lower
base of the cube.

10. RECTANGULAR PARALLELEPIPED

   Definition. *A rectangular parallelepiped is a polyhedron whose six
faces are all rectangles.*

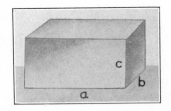

Properties

   1. The parallel edges of a rectangular parallelepiped are equal.

   2. The opposite lateral faces of a rectangular parallelepiped are
equal and parallel.

   3. Any two opposite faces of a rectangular parallelepiped may
be taken as the *bases*.

4. Every section of a rectangular parallelepiped made by a plane parallel to the base is equal in area to that of the base.

Formulas

The total area of a rectangular parallelepiped is equal to the sum of the areas of the faces.

Total area = sum of the areas of faces.

$$T = 2(ab + bc + ca).$$

The volume of a rectangular parallelepiped is equal to the product of the base and the altitude.

Volume = base × altitude.

$$V = abc.$$

Surface analysis. Since each face of a rectangular parallelepiped is a rectangle whose area is the product of its edges and since the opposite faces are equal, the total area of the rectangular parallelepiped with edges a, b, and c is $2(ab + bc + ca)$.

Volume analysis. Consider the rectangular parallelepiped whose dimensions are respectively 2, 3, and 4 units (see figure).

Pass planes parallel to the faces of the solid, dividing the edges into segments one unit long as shown. These planes divide the solid into 2 layers of 12 congruent cubes each, making $3 \times 4 \times 2 = 24$ unit cubes in all. Hence the unit of volume is contained 24 times in the rectangular parallelepiped. This number (24) may be obtained by multiplying together the three dimensions of the rectangular parallelepiped or by multiplying its base by its altitude. When this argument is extended to cover rectangular parallelepipeds of various dimensions, we are led to the following conclusion:

The volume of a rectangular parallelepiped is the product of its three dimensions, or the product of its base and its altitude.

Example 1. A storage room has a rectangular floor 76 ft. by 42 ft. The walls are vertical and 20 ft. high. If there are no windows, find the total area of the ceiling, walls, and floor. Also find the storage space of the room.

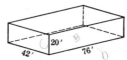

Solution.   The space occupied by the room is a rectangular parallele-piped as shown in the figure.

(*a*) The total surface of a parallelepiped is found by using the formula

$$T = 2(ab + ac + bc).$$

Taking $a = 42$, $b = 76$, $c = 20$, and substituting in this formula, we obtain

$$T = 2[(42)(76) + (42)(20) + (76)(20)],$$

or

$$T = \textbf{11,104 sq. ft.}   Ans.$$

(*b*) The storage space of the room is the volume of the parallele-piped.   The volume of a parallelepiped is found by using the formula

$$V = Bh. \qquad\qquad (a)$$

Consider the area of the floor as base B and the height of the room as altitude h.   Substituting $B = (42)(76)$ and $h = 20$ in formula (*a*), we get

$$V = (42)(76)(20) = \textbf{63,840 cu. ft.}   Ans.$$

Example 2.   Given a rectangular parallelepiped with base a by b and altitude c.   Find the area of a section which contains two diago-nally opposite edges of the parallelepiped.

Solution.   Through the given paral-lelepiped pass a plane containing the two diagonally opposite edges GD and BC, forming the section $GBCD$ shown in the figure.   This section is a rectangle of base GB and altitude $BC = c$.   Since GB is the hypotenuse of right triangle GFB

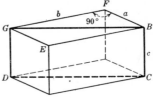

(see figure), we apply the Pythagorean theorem to this triangle and find the length of GB to be

$$GB = \sqrt{a^2 + b^2}.$$

The area of rectangle $GBCD$ is

$$A = BC \times GB.$$

Substituting $BC = c$ and $GB = \sqrt{a^2 + b^2}$ in this equation, we obtain

$$A = c\sqrt{a^2 + b^2}.   Ans.$$

★Example 3.   Solve Ex. 2 if $a = 2.46$ in., $b = 8.68$ in., and $c = 3.71$ in.

Solution using the slide rule or tables. Let angle $FGB = \theta$, and write

$$\tan \theta = \frac{2.46}{8.68}$$

from which we find $\theta = 15° 51'$. By applying the law of sines to the triangle GFB or by using the equation

$$GB = 2.46 \csc \theta,$$

we obtain $GB = 9.02$. Whence $A = (3.71)(9.02) = \mathbf{33.5\ cu.\ in.}$ *Ans.*

PROBLEMS

1. Counting 38 cu. ft. of coal to a ton, how many tons will a coal bin 19 ft. long, 6 ft. wide, and 9 ft. deep contain, when level full?

2. Compute the cost of the lumber necessary to resurface a foot-bridge 16 ft. wide and 150 ft. long with 2-in. planks, if lumber is $40 per 1000 board feet.   Neglect waste.   (One board foot = 1 ft. by 1 ft. by 1 in.)

3. Building bricks are closely stacked in a pile 7 ft. high, 36 ft. long, and 12 ft. wide.   If the bricks are 2 in. by 4 in. by 9 in., how many bricks are in the pile?

4. A packing box 2.2 ft. by 4.9 ft. by 5.5 ft. is to be completely covered with tin.   How many square feet of the metal are needed?   (Neglect waste for seams, etc.)

5. How many cubic yards of material are needed for the foundation of a barn 40 by 80 ft., if the foundation is 2 ft. thick and 12 ft. high?

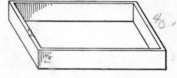

6. A tank, open at the top, is made of sheet iron 1 in. thick.   The internal dimensions of the tank are 4 ft. 8 in. long; 3 ft. 6 in. wide; 4 ft. 4 in. deep.   Find the weight of the tank when empty, and find the weight when full of salt water. (Salt water weighs 64 lb. per cu. ft., and iron is 7.2 times as heavy as salt water.)

7. The edges of a trunk are 3 ft., 4 ft., 6 ft.   A second trunk is twice as long; the other edges are 3 ft., 4 ft.   How do their volumes compare?

8. An electric refrigerator is built in the form of a rectangular parallelepiped.   The inside dimensions are 3 ft. by 2.6 ft. by 1.8 ft.   A freezing unit (1.1 ft. by 0.8 ft. by 0.7 ft.) subtracts from the storage room of the box.   Find the capacity of the refrigerator.

9. A solid concrete porch consists of 3 steps and a landing.   The steps have a tread of 11 in., a rise of 7 in., and a length of 7 ft.; the landing is 6 ft. by 7 ft.   How much material was used in its construction?

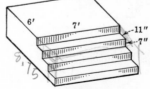

10. Imagine a block of wood to measure 2 ft. by 3 ft. by 4 ft. and to have its total surface area painted blue.   Without the aid of a figure, answer the following questions:

(A) How many times must you cut completely through the block to make cubes which measure 1 ft. on an edge?

(B) How many of the cubes of question (A) will have
    (a) Three blue faces?
    (b) Two blue faces?
    (c) One blue face?
    (d) No blue face?

(C) How many cubes are there in all?

11. Find the length of the diagonal of the parallelepiped considered in Ex. 2. *Hint.* This is the diagonal of the section *GBCD*.

12. In the figure is shown a rectangular parallelepiped whose dimensions are 2, 4, 6. Points *A*, *B*, *C*, *E*, *F*, and *L* are each at the midpoint of an edge. Find the area of each of the sections *ABEF*, *ABC*, and *MNL*.

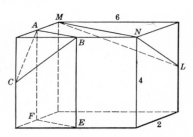

★13. The figure represents a rectangular parallelepiped; *AD* = 20 in., *AB* = 10 in., *AE* = 15 in. (a) Find the number of degrees in the angles *AFB*, *BFO*, *AFO*, *BOF*, *AOF*, *OFC*. (b) Find the area of each of the triangles *ABO*, *BOF*, *AOF*. (c) Find the perpendicular distance from *B* to the plane *AOF*.

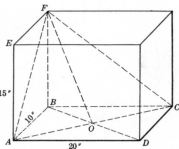

★14. Find the angles that the diagonal of a rectangular parallelepiped 2 in. by 3 in. by 4 in. makes with the faces.

11. CAVALIERI'S THEOREM

In this article we shall discuss a very important theorem known as Cavalieri's theorem. Later we shall see that this theorem is the basis of the analyses of the volumes of most of the solids considered in this book.

So as better to understand Cavalieri's theorem let us, before stating it, consider a pile of uniform cards stacked in the form of a rectangular parallelepiped as shown in Fig. (a). This pile may be distorted into the forms of various irregular solids such

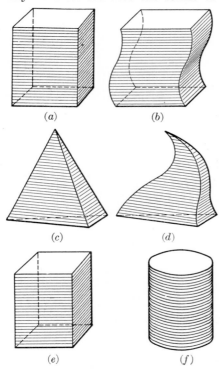

(a)   (b)

(c)   (d)

(e)   (f)

as the one shown in Fig. (b). Obviously the volume of the pile has not been changed.

Now consider a second pile of cards of such size that it is possible to stack them in the form of the solid shown in Fig. (c). Here again we may distort this pile into the forms of various irregular solids such as the one shown in Fig. (d), without changing its volume.

The cards need not be of the same shape in order to afford piles of equal volume. For a pile consisting of 100 square cards would have the same volume as a pile of 100 circular cards [see Figs. (e) and (f)] of the same area and thickness.

Cavalieri's Theorem. *If in two solids of equal altitude the sections made by planes parallel to and at the same distance from their respective bases are always equal, the volumes of the solids are equal.*

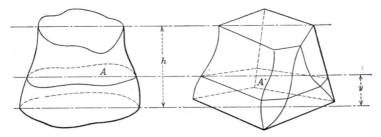

Consider the two solids of equal altitude h shown in the figure. Let A and A' denote corresponding sections which are parallel to and at the same variable distance y from their respective bases. If $A = A'$ the volumes of the two solids are equal.

A proof of Cavalieri's theorem will be found in the Appendix, §49.

12. VOLUME THEOREM

Theorem. *If the bases of a solid are equal in area and lie in parallel planes and every section of the solid parallel to the base is equal in area to that of the base, the volume of the solid is the product of its base and altitude.*

Analysis. Consider the solid CD shown in the figure. Let the bases of this solid lie in parallel planes, and every section parallel to the base be equal in area to the area of the base.

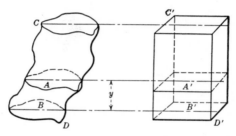

Construct the rectangular parallelepiped $C'D'$ with a base and altitude respectively equal to the base and altitude of the given solid.   Place these solids so that their lower bases lie in the same plane.   Pass a plane parallel to and distant y from the lower bases of the solids cutting the given solid in section A and the parallelepiped in section A'.   Denote the altitude of each solid by h, the base of the given solid by B, and the base of the parallelepiped by B'.   In solid CD we are given

$$A = B,$$

and by Property 4, §10, $A' = B'.$

But by construction $B = B'.$

Therefore $A = A'.$

Since the altitude of each solid is h and since $A = A'$, it follows from Cavalieri's theorem that the volume of solid CD equals the volume of the parallelepiped.   But the volume of the parallelepiped is $B'h = Bh$.   Therefore the volume of solid CD is Bh.

PROBLEMS

1. The solid represented in the figure has square bases of edge a in parallel planes and every section of the solid parallel to the bases is a square of edge a. If its altitude is h, find its volume.

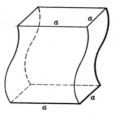

2. A rectangle a by b moves with one of its points on the circumference of a semicircle of radius a, and keeps perpendicular to the bounding diameter of the given semicircle. Find the volume of the solid it generates.

3. A kite is in the form of an equilateral triangle of edge 3 ft. During one part of its flight its center moves on a straight line while the kite remains parallel to its first position. If the distance between the planes of the first and last positions of the kite is 100 ft., find the volume swept out by the kite during this part of its flight.

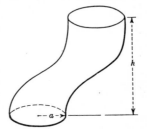

4. The solid shown in the figure has bases which lie in parallel planes. Each base is a circle of radius a, and every section parallel to the bases is also a circle of radius a. If the distance between the bases of the solid is h, write a formula for its volume.

13. PRISM

Definition. *A prism is a polyhedron of which two faces are equal polygons in parallel planes, and the other faces are parallelograms.*

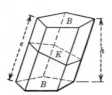

Properties

1. The *bases* are the equal polygons; the *lateral area* is the sum of the areas of the remaining faces.

2. The intersections of the lateral faces are called the *lateral edges*. These lateral edges are equal and parallel.

3. *The sections of a prism made by parallel planes cutting all the lateral edges are equal polygons.*

4. The *altitude* of a prism is the perpendicular distance between the planes of its bases.

5. A *right section* of a prism is a section perpendicular to the lateral edges.

6. A *right prism* is a prism whose lateral edges are perpendicular to its bases; its lateral faces are rectangles.

Unless otherwise stated, in this book when we use the term *cross section* we mean *right section*.

Formulas

The lateral area of a prism is equal to the product of a lateral edge and the perimeter of the right section.

Lateral area = lateral edge × perimeter of right section.

$$S = ep_k.$$

The volume of a prism is equal either to the product of a base and the altitude, or to the product of a right section and a lateral edge.

Volume = base × altitude.

$$V = Bh.$$

Volume = right section × lateral edge.

$$V = Ke.$$

Surface analysis. Each lateral face of a prism is a parallelogram whose area is equal to the product of its base e (edge of prism) and its altitude. This altitude is a side of the right section. Since the sum of all the altitudes of the faces equals the perimeter of the right section, the lateral surface S (the areas of all the lateral faces) equals the perimeter p_k of the right section times the edge e.

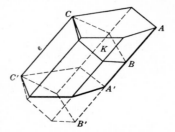

Volume Analysis. Since the bases of a prism are equal in area and lie in parallel planes, and since by Property 3 the area of every section parallel to the base is equal to that of the base, it follows from the Volume theorem (§12) that $V = Bh$.

With the aid of the accompanying figure the student should satisfy himself as to the truth of the formula

$$V = Ke.$$

The usual proof consists essentially in passing the planes CB and $C'B'$ perpendicular to the edge CC' and then showing that the solids CAB and $C'A'B'$ are congruent.

Example. A masonry dam 40 ft. high has a uniform vertical cross section as shown in the figure. The dam is 80 ft. long and its material weighs 125 lb. per cu. ft. Find the weight of the dam.

Solution. The dam is in the form of a prism of altitude 80 ft. with trapezoidal bases. The area of one base is the area of a trapezoid whose bases are 4 ft. and 16 ft. and whose altitude is 40 ft. Hence its area is

$$B = \left(\frac{4 + 16}{2}\right)(40) = 400 \text{ sq. ft.}$$

The volume of the prism is

$$V = Bh = (400)(80) = 32,000 \text{ cu. ft.}$$

Since the masonry weighs 125 lb. per cu. ft., the weight of the dam is

$$W = 125V = (125)(32,000) = \textbf{4,000,000 lb.} \quad Ans.$$

PROBLEMS

1. Let B denote the area of the base of a prism and S the lateral surface; then write a formula for the total surface of a prism.

2. Write a formula for (a) the volume, (b) the total area, of a right prism whose altitude is h and whose base is a square of edge a.

3. A lead pencil whose ends are regular hexagons was cut from a cylindrical piece of wood, with the least waste. If the original piece was 8 in. long and $\frac{1}{2}$ in. in diameter, find the volume of the pencil.

4. Show that every section of a prism made by a plane parallel to its lateral edges is a parallelogram.

5. The lateral surface of a concrete octagonal pier of height 10 ft. is to be resurfaced. If each of the base edges is 1 ft., how many square feet of surfacing will be required?

6. One part of a quartz crystal is a hexagonal prism with a right section of 1.29 sq. in., an edge of 2.31 in., and a base of 1.41 sq. in. Find the altitude of the prism.

7. A trench is 180 ft. long and 12 ft. deep, 7 ft. wide at the top and 4 ft. at the bottom. How many cubic yards of earth have been removed?

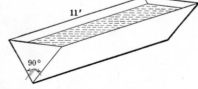

8. A trough is formed by nailing together, edge to edge, two boards 11 ft. in length, so that the right section is a right triangle. If 15 gal. of water are poured into the trough and if the trough is held level so that a right section of the water is an isosceles right triangle, how deep is the water? (231 cu. in. = 1 gal.)

9. A contractor agrees to build a dam, 180 ft. long and 20 ft. high, 12 ft. wide at the bottom and 8 ft. wide at the top, for $9.75 a cubic yard. Find his profit if his costs were $10,000.

10. (a) Find the volume of water in a swimming pool with vertical ends and sides. The length measured at the water line is 50 ft. and the breadth is 20 ft. The bottom of the swimming pool is a plane sloping gradually downward so that the depth of the water at one end is 4 ft. and at the other end is 8 ft.

(b) If the sides, ends, and bottom of the swimming pool are constructed of tile blocks whose glazed surface dimensions are 3 in. by 6 in., and if the ends and sides of the pool extend 2 ft. above the water level, find the number of blocks used if $\frac{1}{20}$ of the surface area is covered by sealing material.

11. A football stand 150 yd. long has 20 tiers of seats; each tier has a rise of 2 ft. and tread of 3 ft. It is constructed of reinforced concrete with a cross section as shown. Find the amount of material used in its construction.

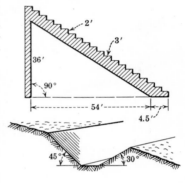

12. A railway cut 200 ft. long and 30 ft. wide at the bottom is made with sloping sides, which are 80 ft. and 60 ft. in length. The 80-ft. side is inclined 45° and the other side is inclined 30° to the horizontal. Find the cost of removing the earth at $2 per load, if the trucks have a capacity of 4 cu. yd.

13. The Pennsylvania Railroad found it necessary, owing to land slides upon the roadbed, to reduce the angle of inclination of one bank of a certain railway cut near Pittsburgh, Pa., from an original angle of 45° to a new angle of 30°. The bank as it originally stood was 200 ft. long and had a slant length of 60 ft. Find the amount of the earth removed, if the top level of the bank remained unchanged.

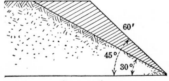

Cross section

14. The trough shown in the figure has triangular ends which lie in parallel planes. The top of the trough is a horizontal rectangle 20 in. by 33 in., and the depth of the trough is 16 in. (a) How many gallons of water will it hold?

(b) How many gallons does it contain when the depth of the water is 10 in.?

(c) What is the depth of the water when the trough contains 3 gal.?

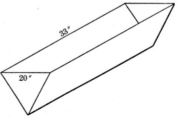

(d) Find the wetted surface when the depth of the water is 9 in. (One gal. = 231 cu. in.)

★**15.** If in Prob. 13 the angle of inclination of the bank was reduced from 40°
to 25°, find the amount of earth removed.

★**16.** A dam 100 ft. long has a cross section which is a trapezoid whose altitude is 16 ft. and whose upper base is 5 ft.   If the lower base angles of the cross
section are 50° and 65°, find the volume of material the dam contains.

★**17.** Show that in any prism the area of a right section is equal to the product
of the base and the sine of the angle between a lateral edge and the base.
(This relation is used in connection with the reflection of light through prisms.)

14. CYLINDRICAL SURFACE

Definition. *A cylindrical surface is a surface generated by a
moving straight line (generator) which is always parallel to a fixed
line, and which always intersects a fixed plane curve (directrix) not
in the plane with the fixed line.*

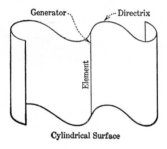
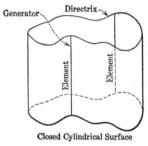

Cylindrical Surface   Closed Cylindrical Surface

Properties

1. An *element* of a cylindrical surface is the generator in any
particular position.

2. If the directrix of a cylindrical surface is a closed curve, the
surface is *closed.*

3. Any line, not an element, tangent to any curve on a cylindrical surface is tangent to the surface.

4. A plane is tangent to a cylindrical surface if it contains an
element of the cylindrical surface and a line tangent to the surface.

15. CYLINDER

Definition. *A cylinder is a solid bounded by a closed cylindrical
surface and two parallel planes.*

Properties

1. The bounding cylindrical surface of a cylinder is called the *lateral surface,* and the two bounding parallel planes are called the *bases.*

2. The bases of a cylinder are equal.

3. The *altitude* of a cylinder is the perpendicular distance between the bases.

4. The sections of a cylinder made by two parallel planes, neither of which cuts a base and both of which cut an element, are congruent.

5. Every section of a cylinder parallel to the base has an area equal to that of the base.

6. The section of a cylinder which contains an element of the cylinder and a point of the cylindrical surface not in this element is a parallelogram. This section contains the element through the given point.

7. The elements of a cylinder are equal.

8. A *right section* of a cylinder is a section perpendicular to all elements of the cylinder.

9. If the bases of a prism are inscribed in the bases of a cylinder, and the lateral edges of the prism are elements of the cylinder, the prism is said to be *inscribed* in the cylinder.

10. If the bases of a prism are circumscribed about the bases of a cylinder, and the lateral edges are parallel to the elements of the cylinder, the prism is said to be *circumscribed* about the cylinder.

Formulas

The lateral area of a cylinder is equal to the product of the perimeter of a right section and an element.

Lateral area = perimeter of right section × element.

$$S = p_k e.$$

The volume of a cylinder is equal either to the product of a base and the altitude, or to the product of an element and a right section.

Volume = base × altitude.

$$V = Bh.$$

Volume = right section × element.

$$V = Ke.$$

Surface analysis. Imagine the lateral area of a cylinder slit along an element and then spread out flat as shown in the figure.

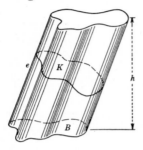

It thus becomes a plane figure having two parallel sides of length e. Since each element of the cylinder is perpendicular to the right section K, the distance between the parallel sides of the developed surface is the perimeter p_k of section K. Each of the other sides is formed by unrolling the perimeter of a base of the cylinder. Hence these sides are equal curves. Any point on one of them is distant e from the corresponding point on the other. Since from these considerations it is evident that area $ABCD$

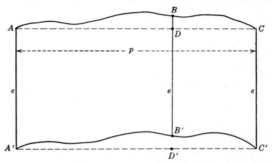

equals area $A'B'C'D'$, the lateral area of the cylinder is equal to the area of rectangle $ACC'A'$. Therefore $S = ep_k$.

Volume analysis. Since the bases of a cylinder are equal in area and lie in parallel planes, and since by Property 5 the area of every section parallel to the base is equal to that of the base, it follows from the Volume theorem (§12) that $V = Bh$.

It is left to the student to show as in the case of the prism that for a cylinder $V = Ke$ also.

Example. A vertical stone column 12.5 ft. high has an elliptical base with the longer axis twice the shorter. If the weight of the column is 12,400 lb. and if the stone weighs 160 lb. per cu. ft., find the area of the largest axial section of the column.

Solution. We first find the area of the elliptical base by means of the formula for an ellipse (see §3),

$$A = \pi ab,$$

where a and b are the dimensions shown in the figure. In this example $b = a/2$. Hence

$$A = \pi(a)\left(\frac{a}{2}\right) = \frac{\pi a^2}{2}.$$

Substituting $B = \dfrac{\pi a^2}{2}$ and $h = 12.5$ in the formula for the volume of a cylinder

$$V = Bh,$$

we get

$$V = \left(\frac{\pi a^2}{2}\right)(12.5). \tag{a}$$

But the volume of the column is also equal to the weight of the column divided by the weight of the stone per cubic foot. Therefore

$$V = \frac{12{,}400}{160}. \tag{b}$$

Equating the values of V from equations (a) and (b), we have

$$\frac{12{,}400}{160} = \left(\frac{\pi a^2}{2}\right)(12.5),$$

from which we obtain

$$a = \sqrt{\frac{(12{,}400)\ (2)}{(160)\ (12.5)\pi}} = 1.9867 \text{ ft.}$$

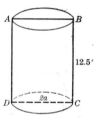

Through the axis of the cylinder pass a plane containing the larger axis of the elliptical base to form the axial section $ABCD$ shown in the figure. This section is a rectangle of base $2a$ and altitude 12.5. Its area is

$$(2a)\ (12.5) = (2)\ (1.9867)\ (12.5) = \textbf{49.668 sq. ft.} \quad Ans.$$

PROBLEMS

1. Find the area of the smallest axial section of the column considered in the example of this article.

2. Prove that every section of a cylinder made by a plane containing two elements is a parallelogram.

3. During a rain, $\frac{1}{4}$ in. of water fell. Find how many gallons of water fell on a level 10-acre park. (Take 1 cu. ft. = 7.48 gal., 1 acre = 43,560 sq. ft.)

4. An ice-storage plant removed from the center of a pond a mass of ice covering an area of 2 acres. If the ice had a uniform thickness of 2 ft., find the weight in tons of the ice removed. (Ice weighs 56 lb. per cu. ft.; 1 ton = 2240 lb.)

5. The average depth of a lake is estimated to be 40 ft. If the surface area is 15 acres, find the volume of water in the lake.

6. An indoor roller-skating rink with an area of 1500 sq. yd. has a concrete flooring 3 in. thick. Find the amount of concrete used in laying the floor.

7. The outer protective smokestack of a steamship is streamlined so that it has a uniform oval section parallel to the deck. The area of this oval section is 48 sq. ft. If the length of the stack is 15 ft. and the stack is raked aft so that its axis at its upper end is horizontally 4.2 ft. from the lower end, find the volume enclosed by the stack. (*Raked* means *inclined.*)

8. The crown of a straw hat has a base of 38 sq. in. The depth of the crown is 3 in. (Inside dimensions are given.) If the head occupies two-thirds of the space enclosed by the crown, find the volume remaining for ventilation.

9. Find the volume of the largest cylinder with circular base that can be inscribed in a cube whose volume is 27 cu. in.

10. A cylinder whose base is a circle is circumscribed about a right prism of altitude 12.6 ft. Find the volume of the cylinder if the base of the prism is (*a*) a square of edge 3 ft., (*b*) a rectangle 3 ft. by 4 ft., (*c*) an equilateral triangle of side 4 ft., (*d*) an isosceles triangle of sides 3 ft., 3 ft., and 2 ft.

★11. Solve Prob. 7 if the length of the stack is 18 ft. and if the axis is inclined 76° 15′ to the horizontal.

16. CIRCULAR CYLINDER

Definition. *A circular cylinder is a cylinder which has a circular right section.*

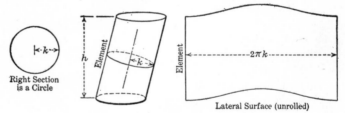

Right Section is a Circle

Lateral Surface (unrolled)

Properties

If a prism whose right section is a regular polygon is inscribed in or circumscribed about a circular cylinder, and if the number of sides of the right section of the prism is indefinitely increased in such a way that every side approaches zero, the volume of the cylinder is the limit of the volume of the prism; the lateral area of the cylinder is the limit of the lateral area of the prism; the perimeter of a base of the cylinder is the limit of the perimeter of a base of the prism.

Formulas

The lateral area of a circular cylinder is equal to the product of the perimeter of a right section and an element.

Lateral area = perimeter of right section × element.

$$S = p_k e.$$

The volume of a circular cylinder is equal to the product of either a right section and an element, or the base and the altitude.

Volume = base × altitude.

$$V = Bh.$$

Volume = right section × element.

$$V = Ke.$$

Example. A pole in the form of a circular cylinder of altitude 18 ft. and diameter of right section 0.4 ft. has a base whose largest dimension is 0.5 ft. If the pole rolls until it has covered an area of level ground, equal to that of one acre, how many revolutions will it make?

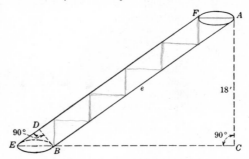

Solution. Through the axis of the cylinder pass a plane containing FA, the longer dimension of the upper base (see figure). In this plane drop perpendicular AC to EB produced and drop perpendicular BD to EF. Since the sides of angles DEB and ABC are respectively parallel, angle DEB = angle CBA. Whence right triangles ABC and DEB are similar. Therefore

$$\frac{AB}{18} = \frac{EB}{DB} = \frac{0.5}{0.4},$$

or $$AB = 22.5.$$

The right section of the cylinder is a circle of diameter 0.4 ft. Hence its perimeter $p_k = 0.4\pi$.

Substituting $p = 0.4\pi$ and $e = AB = 22.5$ in the formula

$$S = p_k e,$$

we obtain

$$S = (0.4\pi)\,(22.5) = 9\pi \text{ sq. ft.}$$

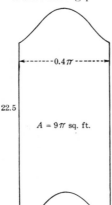

This is the lateral surface of the pole and hence is the area of level ground covered in one revolution (see figure). To find the number of revolutions n, made when the pole rolls over an acre ($= 43,560$ sq. ft.), we write

$$n\,(9\pi) = 43,560$$

or

$$n = \frac{43,560}{9\pi} = \textbf{1540.6 revolutions.} \quad Ans.$$

PROBLEMS

1. A pine log 40 ft. long has a uniform circular cross section of radius 11 in. The ends lie in parallel planes which are not perpendicular to the axis of the log. How much paint will be required to give the log (ends not included) two coats, if 1 gal. of paint covers 800 sq. ft. of surface? If pine weighs 31 lb. per cu. ft., find the weight of the log.

2. A straight stairway has a balustrade, with dimensions as shown, containing 2 circular balusters to a step. The foot and hand rails are parallel. Find the total amount of wood used and the total area to be painted, neglecting the rails.

14 Steps

3. A circular concrete conduit, whose inside diameter is 10 ft., is 1 ft. thick. It rises 16 ft. per 1000 horizontal feet. The vertical plane which contains the axis is perpendicular to the two vertical planes which contain the ends of the conduit. If the ends are 3000 ft. apart, find the amount of concrete used in the construction of the conduit.

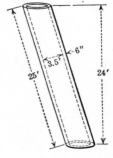

4. A smokestack of a ship is 25 ft. long with a rake aft (angle of the stack's inclination from the vertical) so that its top rises 24 ft. above the deck. The cross section of the flue is a circle with a diameter of $3\frac{1}{2}$ ft. Completely encircling the flue is a protective stack. The distance between the two stacks is 6 in. Find the space enclosed between the two stacks and also the outside painting surface of the protective stack. (Neglect the thickness of the metal.)

5. A channel, whose cross section is a semicircle, with a rise of 1 ft. per 1000 ft., is flowing full. The diameter of the channel is 6.55 ft. The vertical plane which contains the axis is perpendicular to the two vertical planes which contain the ends of the channel. If the end planes are 2000 ft. apart, find the amount of water in the channel.

6. Two vertical brine tanks, with tops on the same level, one 16 ft. deep, the other 4 ft. deep, have their tops and bottoms connected by pipes 2 in. in diameter. If the pipe connecting the tops measures 5 ft., find the weight of brine in the other pipe when entirely full. (The brine weighs 66.8 lb. per cu. ft.)

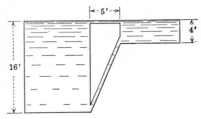

★7. An air duct in the form of a circular cylinder has a cross section of diameter 16 in. The distance between the bases is 20 ft., and the elements are inclined at an angle of 50° to the bases. Find the amount of magnesia required to protect the duct with a magnesia covering ½ in. thick.

17. RIGHT CIRCULAR CYLINDER

Definition. *A right circular cylinder is a circular cylinder whose elements are perpendicular to its base.*

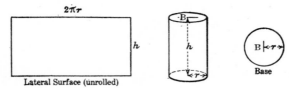

Lateral Surface (unrolled)   Base

Properties

1. The *axis* of a right circular cylinder is the line joining the centers of the bases.

2. A right circular cylinder may be generated by the revolution of a rectangle about one side as an axis, and is therefore also called a *cylinder of revolution.*

3. The center of any section of a right circular cylinder parallel to the base is on the axis.

4. Any element of a right circular cylinder is equal to its altitude.

5. Every section of a right circular cylinder made by a plane containing an element is a rectangle.

Formulas

The lateral area of a right circular cylinder is the product of its altitude and the circumference of its base.

Lateral area = altitude × circumference of base.

$$S = hc.$$

The volume of a right circular cylinder is the product of the area of the base and its altitude.

Volume = base × altitude.

$$V = Bh.$$

Example 1.   Express the lateral surface S and the volume V of a right circular cylinder in terms of the radius of the base r and the altitude h.

Solution.   For the circular base we have

$$\text{Circumference } c = 2\pi r.$$

Therefore

$$S = 2\pi r h.   Ans.$$

Substituting $B = \pi r^2$ in the formula

$$V = Bh,$$

we obtain

$$V = \pi r^2 h.   Ans.$$

Example 2.   An iron pipe 10 ft. long has an internal diameter of 1 ft.   If the iron is $\frac{1}{2}$ in. thick, find the volume of metal in the pipe.

Solution.   From the figure we observe that the volume of metal required is the difference between the volumes of two right circular cylinders of the same altitude. Therefore, if we denote the required volume by V, the volume of the larger cylinder by V_1, and the volume of the smaller cylinder by V_2, we write

$$V = V_1 - V_2.$$

Since for a cylinder $V = Bh$, we have

$$V = B_1 h - B_2 h,$$

where B_1 and B_2 are the areas of the bases of the two cylinders.   But in terms of diameters $B_1 = \dfrac{\pi d_1^2}{4}$ and $B_2 = \dfrac{\pi d_2^2}{4}$.   Therefore we have

$$V = \frac{\pi d_1^2}{4} h - \frac{\pi d_2^2}{4} h = \frac{\pi}{4} h(d_1^2 - d_2^2) = \frac{\pi}{4} h \, (d_1 + d_2)(d_1 - d_2). \qquad (a)$$

But $h = 10$ ft., $d_1 = 12 + (2)\left(\frac{1}{2}\right) = 13$ in. $= \frac{13}{12}$ ft., and $d_2 = 1$ ft. Substituting these values in equation (a), we have

$$V = \frac{\pi}{4}\,10\left[\left(\frac{13}{12}+1\right)\left(\frac{13}{12}-1\right)\right] = \mathbf{1.3635\ cu.\ ft.}\quad Ans.$$

PROBLEMS

1. The diameter of a well is 6 ft., and the water is 7 ft. deep. How many gallons of water are there in the well, reckoning 7.48 gal. to the cubic foot?

2. A paint manufacturer desires a cylindrical steel drum to hold 50 gal. of roof paint. For convenience in handling, it is found necessary to limit the inside diameter to $2\frac{1}{2}$ ft. Find the height of the drum desired. (One gal. = 231 cu. in.)

3. Find the waste in making the largest possible cylindrical rod from a bar of iron 3 ft. long which has a square cross section whose diagonal is 6 in.

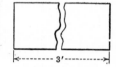

4. A cubic foot of water weighs about 62.4 lb. What must be the diameter of a cylindrical pail 1 ft. high in order for it to hold the water from 25 lb. of ice? How many square inches of sheet tin are required to make the pan? (Neglect waste in cutting and lapping.)

5. If a lead pipe $\frac{1}{4}$ in. thick has an inner diameter of $1\frac{1}{2}$ in., find the number of cubic inches of lead in a piece of pipe 10 ft. long.

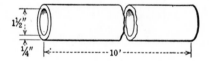

6. A certain factory manufactures tin cans. It received an order for 10,000 cylindrical tin cans of height 5 in. and diameter 3 in. How many square feet of tin did this order require if 7 sq. in. are allowed for waste and seams in each can?

7. A gas company erected a new gasholder. The gasholder (top and sides) was given three coats of paint. It took 50 bbl. of paint of 50 gal. each to complete the work. The height of the tank was 160 ft. and the diameter of the base was 218 ft. If the paint cost $1 per gallon, what was the cost per square yard of surface?

8. A circular oak table top is 4 ft. in diameter and $\frac{3}{4}$ in. thick. How heavy is it if oak weighs 47 lb. per cu. ft.?

9. A log with a circular cross section is 15 ft. long and 27 in. in diameter at the smaller end. Find the dimensions of the largest piece of timber of length 15 ft. with a uniform square cross section, that can be cut from the log.

343000 = 4 Π R (ΔR)

7½ gal = 1 cu ft.

10. A cylindrical standpipe is to contain 343,000 gal. of water. If its height is to be twice its diameter, what must be its dimensions?

11. When a body is immersed in water in a right circular cylinder 60 cm. in diameter, the level of the water rises 40 cm. What is the volume of the body?

12. A right cylindrical solid of altitude 6 in. has the cross section shown in the shaded portion of the figure. $BEDG$ is a circle whose radius is OG. $AFCG$ is a circle which is tangent to the larger circle at G. If $AB = CD = 5$ in. and if $EF = 9$ in., find the volume of the cylinder.

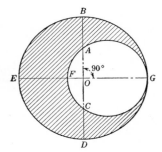
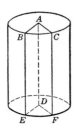

13. A wedge $ABCDEF$ (see figure) is cut from a right circular cylindrical block of altitude 10 in. and radius 4 in. The dihedral angle of the wedge is 30°. Calculate its volume and total surface.

14. Pass a plane through a cube of edge 6 in. so that the section formed will be a regular hexagon. Find the volume of a right circular cylinder 8 in. long, (*a*) whose base circumscribes this hexagon, (*b*) whose base is inscribed in this hexagon.

15. Find the volume of the largest right circular cylinder that can be circumscribed about a rectangular parallelepiped of dimensions 2 ft. by 3 ft. by 4 ft.

★**16.** If the angle of the wedge in Prob. 13 is 42° 30′, find the volume and total area of the wedge.

18. MISCELLANEOUS PROBLEMS

1. A trench is 200 ft. long and 12 ft. deep, 8 ft. wide at the top and 4 ft. wide at the bottom. How many cubic yards of earth have been removed?

2. When an irregular-shaped rock is placed in a cylindrical vessel of water whose radius is 4.18 in., the water rises 6.85 in. What is the volume of the rock if it is completely submerged?

3. A dam is 40 ft. long, 12 ft. high, 7 ft. wide at the bottom, and 4 ft. wide at the top. How many cubic yards of material were used in constructing it?

4. Two rectangular water tanks with tops on the same level are connected by a pipe through their bottoms. The base of one is 6 in. higher than that of the other. Their dimensions are 4 by 5 by 2½ ft. and 4 by 7 by 3 ft., respectively. How deep is the water in the larger tank when the water they contain equals half their combined capacity, if the 2½-ft. and 3-ft. edges are vertical?

5. A cylindrical tin can holding 2 gal. has its height equal to the diameter of its base. Another cylindrical tin can with the same capacity has its height equal to twice the diameter of its base. Find the ratio of the amount of tin required for making the two cans with covers.

6. How much wood is wasted in turning out the largest possible cylindrical rod from a stick whose uniform square cross-sectional area is 10 sq. in. and whose length is 5 ft.?

7. How long a wire 0.1 in. in diameter can be drawn from a block of copper 2 by 4 by 6 in.?

8. A piece of lead pipe is 50 ft. long. Its outer radius is 2 in., and it is $\frac{1}{4}$ in. thick. Into how many spherical bullets $\frac{1}{4}$ in. in diameter can it be melted?

9. A corncrib 20 ft. long has a cross section which is represented in the figure. The crib is entirely filled with corn on the ear. How many bushels of corn does it contain, if 2 bu. of corn on the ear are equal to 1 bu. of shelled corn? (Use the approximation, 1 bu. = $1\frac{1}{4}$ cu. ft.)

10. How many bricks each 8 in. by $2\frac{3}{4}$ in. by 2 in. will be required to build a wall 22 ft. by 3 ft. by 2 ft. (not allowing for mortar)?

11. The height of a hot-water boiler attached to a furnace is $5\frac{1}{2}$ ft. The circumference of the boiler is 48 in. If the metal is $\frac{1}{8}$ in. thick, how many gallons will the boiler contain when full? (One gal. = 231 cu. in.)

12. A cylindrical tank, diameter 1 ft., length 6 ft., is placed so that its axis is horizontal. How many pounds of water will be used in filling it to a depth of 9 in., if water weighs 62.4 lb. per cu. ft.?

13. How many washers can be made from a cube of metal 4 in. on a side, if the washers are $\frac{5}{8}$ in. in diameter and $\frac{1}{8}$ in. thick? The hole in the center of the washers is $\frac{1}{4}$ in. in diameter.

14. What are the dimensions of a gallon can of uniform square cross section whose height is twice the length of an edge of its base? (One gal. equals 231 cu. in.)

15. A woodman makes a wedge-shaped cut in the trunk of a tree. Assume that the trunk is a right circular cylinder of radius 4 in., that the lower surface of the cut is a horizontal plane, and that the upper surface is a plane inclined at an angle of 45° to the horizontal and intersecting the lower surface of the cut in a diameter. This wedge is then cut into two equal pieces by a vertical cut. What is the area of this vertical section? The woodman now wishes to divide one of these pieces by another section parallel to the first section. If the new section is to have an area equal to one-fourth that of the original section, where should the cut be made?

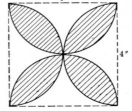

16. How deep a cut should be milled off one side of a $2\frac{1}{2}$-in. shaft to make a flat (a rectangular flat area) $1\frac{1}{8}$ in. wide?

17. The base of a right cylinder is shown in the figure. It is formed by describing semicircular arcs within the square upon the four sides as diameters. If the altitude of the cylinder is 12 in., find the volume and total area.

18. Using the vertices of a 9-in. square as centers, and radii equal to 3 in., four quadrants are described within the square. If the figure thus formed is the uniform cross section of a cylinder of element 7 in., find the volume and total area of the cylinder.

19. Using the vertices of a 9-in. square as centers, and radii equal to 3 in., four arcs are described outside the square. If the figure thus formed is the uniform cross section of cylinder of element 7 in., find the volume and total area of the cylinder.

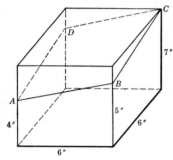

20. A right prism of altitude 7 in. and square base 6 in. on an edge is cut by a plane forming section $ABCD$ as shown. (*a*) Find the length of the diagonal AC. ★(*b*) Find angle ABC. (*c*) Find the area of section $ABCD$. ★(*d*) Find the angle which the plane of the section $ABCD$ makes with the plane of the base.

21. In the figure is shown a block of wood in the form of a right prism whose bases are right triangles. A cylindrical auger hole of diameter 2 in. is

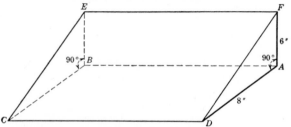

bored through the block. If the elements of the cylindrical hole are perpendicular to face $ABEF$ and if the lateral surface of the cylindrical hole is tangent to face $ABCD$, find the volume removed.

22. The figure represents a truncated prism. The base $ABCD$ is a square, and the lateral edges AE, BF, CG, DH are perpendicular to the base. $AB = 10$ in., $AE = 6$ in., $BF = 10$ in., $CG = 10$ in., $DH = 6$ in. Find (*a*) the length of each face diagonal; ★(*b*) each face angle; (*c*) the length of each diagonal of the solid; (*d*) the lateral area; (*e*) the total area; ★(*f*) the angle BFH; (*g*) the volume.

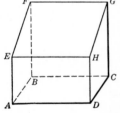

23. The figure shows a right section of a railroad cut in a hillside. If the sides rise 1 unit vertically to a horizontal distance of

1.5 units, and if the length of the cut is 100 ft., find the volume of earth removed.

★**24.** Find the angles that the diagonal of a rectangular parallelepiped 1 in. by 3 in. by 5 in. make with the faces.

★**25.** At what angle with the horizontal must the base of a right circular cylinder be tilted to make it just topple over if its diameter is 12 ft. and its altitude is 16 ft.? (The center of gravity is at the middle point C of the axis of the cylinder. The base must be tilted so that the line AC becomes vertical.)

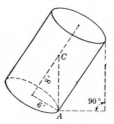

★**26.** The plumb-line distance from the lowest point of the top of the Leaning Tower of Pisa to the ground is 179 ft. The tower leans so that this plumb line strikes the ground 14 ft. from the nearest point of the base as shown. (a) At what angle is its axis now inclined from the vertical? (b) At what angle would its axis have to be inclined from the vertical before it would topple over? See Prob. 25.

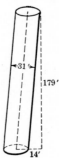

CHAPTER IV

SOLIDS FOR WHICH $V = \frac{1}{3}Bh$

19. INTRODUCTION

In this chapter we deal with a class of solids whose volumes are found by means of the formula $V = \frac{1}{3}Bh$, and discuss the important relations which exist among similar figures.

20. PYRAMID

Definition. *A pyramid is a polyhedron of which one face, called the base, is a polygon of any number of sides and the other faces are triangles which have a common vertex.*

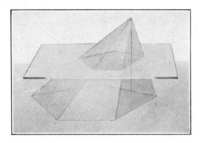 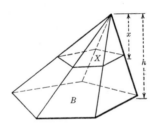

Properties

1. The triangular faces are called the *lateral faces.*

2. The *altitude* of a pyramid is the length of the perpendicular dropped from the vertex to the plane of the base.

3. If a pyramid is cut by a plane parallel to the base, the lateral edges and the altitude are divided proportionally; the section is a polygon similar to the base; and the areas of two such sections are to each other as the squares of their distances from the vertex. The base itself may be considered one of the sections in question. In symbols we write $\dfrac{X}{B} = \dfrac{x^2}{h^2}$ (see figure).

4. If two pyramids have equal bases and equal altitudes, by Property 3, we can show that the area of the section of one pyramid

46

parallel to the base is equal to the area of the corresponding section of the other. Hence in accordance with Cavalieri's theorem the two pyramids are equivalent.

Formulas

The lateral area of a pyramid is equal to the sum of the areas of the lateral faces of the pyramid.

$$S = sum\ of\ areas\ of\ faces.$$

The volume of any pyramid is equal to one-third the product of the base and the altitude.

$$Volume = \tfrac{1}{3}\ base \times altitude.$$
$$V = \tfrac{1}{3}Bh.$$

Surface analysis. Each of the lateral faces of a pyramid is a triangle. The lateral area is the sum of the areas of these triangular faces.

Volume analysis. Let the solid $E\text{-}AGC$ shown in the figure be a triangular pyramid. Complete the prism $EFD\text{-}AGC$ by passing a plane through base edge AC parallel to the opposite lateral edge EG, and by passing another plane through the vertex E parallel to the base AGC. The prism $AGC\text{-}DEF$ has the same base B

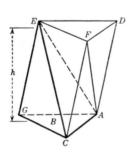
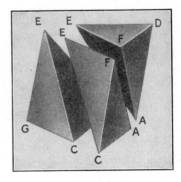

and altitude h as the given pyramid. The plane AFE cuts the part added (see figure) into two triangular pyramids, each equivalent to the given pyramid; for $E\text{-}AGC$ and $A\text{-}DEF$ have the same altitude as the prism, and have the bottom and top of the prism respectively as bases, while $E\text{-}AFC$ and $E\text{-}AFD$ have the same altitude and equal bases (Property 4). Hence the volume of the given pyramid is one-third the volume of the constructed prism. But the volume of the prism = Bh. Therefore the volume of the

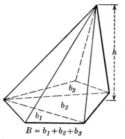

given pyramid (any triangular pyramid) = $\frac{1}{3}Bh$.

We can divide any pyramid into triangular pyramids (see figure) by passing planes through one lateral edge, and all the other lateral edges excepting the two edges adjacent to this one. Each of these triangular pyramids has an altitude equal to the altitude of the given pyramid, and the base of the given pyramid is the sum of the bases of

$B = b_1 + b_2 + b_3$

the triangular pyramids. Hence for the given pyramid $V = \frac{1}{3}$ (sum of bases of triangular pyramids) $h = \frac{1}{3}Bh$.

Example. The pyramidal slice of earth shown in the figure was removed from a railway embankment. Find the volume of earth removed.

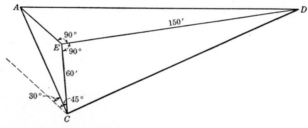

Solution. If we consider triangle AEC as base of the slice, DE is the altitude. From an end view of the base (see figure) we see that EE' and $E'C$ are the legs of a 45° right triangle whose hypotenuse is 60 ft. Hence

$$EE' = E'C = \frac{60}{\sqrt{2}}.$$

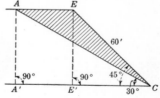

Since $A'C$ and AA' are the legs of a 30°–60° right triangle and $AA' = EE' = \dfrac{60}{\sqrt{2}}$, we have

$$A'C = \sqrt{3}\, AA' = (\sqrt{3})\left(\frac{60}{\sqrt{2}}\right).$$

But $AE = A'C - E'C = (\sqrt{3})\left(\dfrac{60}{\sqrt{2}}\right) - \dfrac{60}{\sqrt{2}}.$

Considering AE as the base and EE' as the altitude of triangle AEC, we find its area to be

$$\tfrac{1}{2}(AE)\,(EE') = \tfrac{1}{2}\left[(\sqrt{3})\left(\frac{60}{\sqrt{2}}\right) - \frac{60}{\sqrt{2}}\right]\frac{60}{\sqrt{2}} = 658.89 \text{ sq. ft.}$$

Substituting $B = 658.89$ and $h = 150$ in the formula

$$V = \tfrac{1}{3}Bh,$$

we find

$$V = \tfrac{1}{3}(658.89)\,(150) = \textbf{32,944 cu. ft.} \quad Ans.$$

PROBLEMS

1. If a pyramid of base B has its vertex at any point in a plane parallel to and distant h from the plane of the base, find its volume.

2. In the corner of a cellar is a pyramidal heap of coal. The base of the heap is an isosceles right triangle whose hypotenuse is 20 ft., and the altitude of the heap is 7 ft. If there are 35 cu. ft. in a ton of coal, how many tons are there in this heap?

3. A pottery manufacturer has an order to manufacture 5000 hanging vases each to hold $\tfrac{1}{6}$ pt. of water when full. The vases are designed so as to fit into the corner of a room. The faces of each vase are triangular in shape and intersect to form a pointed bottom. The area of the polygon cut out of the plane of the base by the lateral faces is 3 sq. in. The height of the vase is 8 in. Compute the weight of pottery required if pottery weighs 130 lb. per cu. ft.

4. A pyramidal book end made of composition material has a base in the shape of an irregular polygon whose measurements are shown in the sketch. The faces are triangles whose vertices are coincident. The common vertex is in the plane of the face against which the books rest. This latter face is at right angles to the base and has an altitude of 7 in. and a base of $4\tfrac{1}{2}$ in. Find the amount of material in 1000 pairs of such book ends.

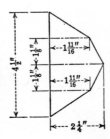

5. The coal considered in Prob. 2 just fills a rectangular bin whose floor is 7 ft. by 6 ft. Find the depth of the coal.

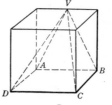

6. A pyramid V–$ABCD$ is cut from a cube of edge 12 in., as shown in the figure. The vertex V is the midpoint of an upper edge of the cube. Compute the lateral surface of the pyramid.

7. If a plane is passed through the vertices A, B, and C of the cube shown in the figure, show that the volume of the pyramid cut off is one-sixth that of the cube.

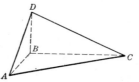

★8. In the pyramid shown in the figure, $AB = 9$ in., $BC = 12$ in., and $BD = 5$ in. The three face angles at B are each 90°. Calculate the three face angles at A and the total surface of the solid.

★9. Solve the example of this article by using 20° and 35° instead of 30° and 45°, respectively.

21. REGULAR PYRAMID

Definition. *A regular pyramid is one whose base is a regular polygon whose center coincides with the foot of the perpendicular dropped from the vertex to the base.*

Lateral Face

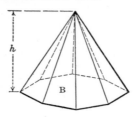

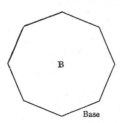

Base

Properties

1. The lateral edges of a regular pyramid are equal.

2. The lateral faces of a regular pyramid are congruent isosceles triangles.

3. The altitudes of the lateral faces of a regular pyramid are equal.

4. The *slant height* of a regular pyramid is the altitude of a lateral face.

5. The *altitude* of a regular pyramid is equal to the length of the perpendicular dropped from the vertex to the center of the base.

6. If a regular pyramid is cut by a plane parallel to its base the pyramid cut off is a regular pyramid.

Formulas

The lateral area of a regular pyramid is equal to one-half the product of the perimeter of the base and the slant height.

Lateral area = ½ perimeter of base × slant height.

$$S = \tfrac{1}{2}pl.$$

The volume of a regular pyramid is equal to one-third the product of the base and the altitude.

Volume = ⅓ base × altitude.

$$V = \tfrac{1}{3}Bh.$$

Surface analysis. In a regular pyramid, let S be the lateral area, let l be the slant height, and let p be the perimeter of the base. Since the faces of the pyramid are equal isosceles triangles with a common altitude l, and since the sum of the bases of these triangles equals p, the sum of the areas of faces is $S = \tfrac{1}{2}pl$.

Example. Given a regular tetrahedron (a triangular pyramid all of whose faces are equilateral triangles) of edge a; find its altitude.

Solution. Through tetrahedron A–BCD pass a plane containing AB and altitude AE, forming section ABE' shown in the figure. By Property 5, E is the center of the base BCD. Since the base of a regular tetrahedron is an equilateral triangle, from plane geometry E is the point of intersection of the perpendicular bisectors of the sides of the triangle. These perpendicular bisectors in the case of an equilateral triangle coincide with the medians.

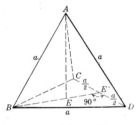

Applying the Pythagorean theorem to the right triangle $BE'D$, we get

$$BE' = \sqrt{a^2 - \left(\frac{a}{2}\right)^2} = \frac{a}{2}\sqrt{3}.$$

Since from plane geometry the medians of a triangle meet in a point which is two thirds of the distance from each vertex to the midpoint of the opposite side, we have

$$BE = \tfrac{2}{3}BE' = \tfrac{2}{3}\left(\frac{a}{2}\sqrt{3}\right) = \frac{a\sqrt{3}}{3}.$$

In right triangle ABE, $AB = a$ and $BE = \dfrac{a\sqrt{3}}{3}$.   Therefore

$$AE = \sqrt{a^2 - \left(\frac{a\sqrt{3}}{3}\right)^2} = a\sqrt{\tfrac{2}{3}}. \quad Ans.$$

PROBLEMS

1. If there are $1\frac{1}{4}$ cu. ft. in a bushel, what is the capacity (in bushels) of a hopper in the shape of an inverted pyramid 12 ft. deep and 8 ft. square at the top?

2. A church spire in the form of a regular hexagonal pyramid whose base edge is 8 ft. and whose altitude is 75 ft. is to be painted at a cost of 22 cents per square yard.   What is the total cost?

The Pyramids on the Nile, Egypt.

3. The regular pyramidal roof of the Washington Monument is 55 ft. high and has a base which is a square 35 ft. 2 in. on a side.   The marble slabs of which it is built weigh 165 lb. per cu. ft.   If the room covered by the roof is a pyramid whose square base is 34 ft. on a side and 54 ft. high, what is the weight of the roof?   (Neglect the six small windows.)

4. The altitude of the great Pyramid of Cheops in Egypt originally was 480 ft. and its square base was 764 ft. on an edge.   It is said to have cost $10 a cubic yard and $3 more for each square yard of lateral surface (considered as planes).   What was its cost?

5. The roof of a water tower is composed of 6 equal isosceles triangles whose vertices meet in the center of the roof.   If the inclined edges measure 17 ft. and the height of the roof is 8 ft., find the number of square feet of tar paper necessary to cover the roof.   (Neglect the waste in lapping, cutting, etc.)

6. How may 6 matches be arranged so as to form 4 equal, equilateral triangles having a match as an edge?   In this position these matches may be considered as the edges of a certain solid.   What is it?

7. The illustration shows the monument of Cestius in Rome, which is a square pyramid 121½ ft. high with a base edge measuring 98.4 ft.   Find the number of square feet in the lateral surface of the monument.   What is its volume?

The Monument of Cestius in Rome.

8. Find the area of the base of a regular square pyramid whose lateral faces are equilateral triangles and whose altitude is 8 in.

9. Find the volume of a regular tetrahedron of edge a.

10. Show how a cube can be made up of 6 congruent pyramids whose lateral edges lie along the diagonals of the cube.

11. A pyramid has its vertex at the center of a cube and its base coincides with a face of the cube.   Find the angle that each lateral face of the pyramid makes with the base of the pyramid.

22. SIMILAR FIGURES

Definition. *Similar polyhedrons are polyhedrons that have the same number of faces, respectively similar and similarly placed, and*

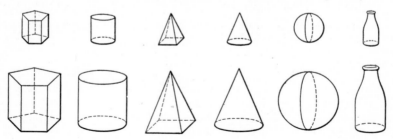

have their corresponding polyhedral angles equal.

Corresponding lines of similar figures are proportional.

Formulas

The areas of similar plane figures or similar surfaces (s, S) have the same ratio as the squares of any two corresponding lines (x, X).

$$\frac{s}{S} = \frac{x^2}{X^2}.$$

The volumes of similar solids (v, V) have the same ratio as the cubes of any two corresponding lines (x, X).

$$\frac{v}{V} = \frac{x^3}{X^3}.$$

In similar figures of any kind, pairs of corresponding line segments such as x, X, and y, Y have the same ratio.

$$\frac{x}{X} = \frac{y}{Y}.$$

Analysis.   Consider the two similar rectangular parallelepipeds whose dimensions are $a \times b \times c$ and $ar \times br \times cr$, respectively. Denote the volume of the former by V_1 and the volume of the latter by V_2.   From §10, we have

$$V_1 = (a)(b)(c) = abc \tag{1}$$

and

$$V_2 = (ar)(br)(cr) = abc(r^3). \tag{2}$$

Dividing equation (1) by equation (2), member by member, we have

$$\frac{V_1}{V_2} = \frac{abc}{abc(r^3)} = \frac{1}{r^3}. \tag{3}$$

Multiplying both numerator and denominator of the right-hand member of (3) first by a^3, then by b^3, and finally by c^3, we obtain

$$\frac{V_1}{V_2} = \frac{a^3}{(ar)^3}, \quad \frac{V_1}{V_2} = \frac{b^3}{(br)^3}, \quad \frac{V_1}{V_2} = \frac{c^3}{(cr)^3}.$$

By using an extension of this argument, together with the theory of limits, it can be shown that the volumes of similar solids have the same ratio as the cubes of any two corresponding line segments.

Similarly we can show that the areas of similar plane figures or similar surfaces have the same ratio as the squares of any two corresponding line segments.

Example. A pyramid of altitude h and base B is divided into three parts by two planes passed parallel to the base. If these planes are distant $h/3$ and $2h/3$, respectively, from the vertex, find the ratio of the volume of the middle part to the volume of the largest part.

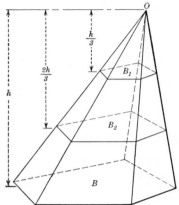

Solution. The sections of the pyramid formed by the planes are denoted by B_1 and B_2 in the figure. Consider the three pyramids O–B_1, O–B_2, and O–B. Denote their volumes by V_1, V_2, and V_3, respectively. From the construction and considerations of this article we observe that these pyramids are similar. Therefore in the formula

$$\frac{v}{V} = \frac{x^3}{X^3}$$

we substitute $v = V_1$, $V = V_2$, $x = h/3$, and $X = 2h/3$ to get

$$\frac{V_1}{V_2} = \frac{\left(\dfrac{h}{3}\right)^3}{\left(\dfrac{2h}{3}\right)^3} = \frac{1}{8} \; ; \tag{a}$$

and substitute $v = V_1$, $V = V_3$, $x = h/3$, and $X = h$ to get

$$\frac{V_1}{V_3} = \frac{\left(\dfrac{h}{3}\right)^3}{h^3} = \frac{1}{27} . \tag{b}$$

In terms of the symbols denoting the volumes of the three pyramids, the required ratio is

$$\frac{V_2 - V_1}{V_3 - V_2} . \tag{c}$$

From equations (a) and (b) we obtain

$$V_2 = 8V_1 \quad \text{and} \quad V_3 = 27V_1.$$

Substituting these values of V_2 and V_3 in (c), we get

$$\frac{8V_1 - V_1}{27V_1 - 8V_1} = \frac{7V_1}{19V_1} = \frac{\mathbf{7}}{\mathbf{19}}. \quad Ans.$$

PROBLEMS

1. A globe 1 ft. in diameter is how many times as large as a marble 1 in. in diameter?

2. The diameter of the earth is 7920 miles, and that of the moon is 2160 miles. Compare their volumes.

3. Two cylindrical boilers are similar, and the diameter of one is twice the diameter of the other. What is the ratio of their lateral surfaces and of the areas of their cross sections?

4. A cube of ice is 2 ft. by 2 ft. by 2 ft. The ice melts until it becomes a cube which is one-half as heavy as the original. Find the dimensions of the new cube.

5. The inside dimensions of a box are 2 by 3 by 4 ft. Find the dimensions of a packing box of the same shape which will hold 8 times as much.

6. A tank in the form of a right circular cone is 3 ft. high and its base is 2 ft. in radius. It is desired to build a similar tank whose volume is twice as great. What should be the dimensions of the larger tank?

7. A manufacturer receives an order for 2000 souvenirs which are to be miniature models of the Washington Monument. Each must be exactly similar to the original monument and must be 4 in. high. If the models are solid, find the amount of material necessary to fill the order. (Take 1,038,800 cu. ft. as volume of Washington Monument, 555 ft. as height.)

8. Which is the more heavily built, a man 5½ ft. tall who weighs 160 lb. or one 6 ft. tall who weighs 200 lb.?

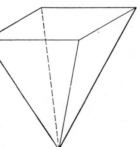

9. If a child 2½ ft. in height weighs 30 lb., what would be the weight of a man 5 ft. tall of the same proportions?

10. The pyramidal tank shown in the figure has a square base 11.6 ft. on a side and an altitude of 14.8 ft. How many gallons of water are in it when the depth of the water is 5.725 ft.?

11. What fraction of the volume of a pyramid must be cut off by a plane parallel to the base if the pyramid thus formed has a lateral area equal to one-half of the lateral area of the original pyramid?

12. A pyramid whose altitude is 4 ft. weighs 600 lb. At what distance from its vertex must it be cut by a plane parallel to its base so that two solids of equal weight will be formed?

13. The volume of a certain solid is 1200 cu. in. and its surface is 800 sq. in. What will be the surface of a similar solid whose volume is 2400 cu. in.?

14. A steamship 790 ft. long has a tonnage of 32,500, and another 882 ft. long has a tonnage of 45,000. Can these vessels be similar in shape? If not, which has the greater tonnage in proportion to its length?

15. In a laboratory experiment a heavy iron ball is suspended by a steel wire. In suspending another ball of twice the diameter a wire of twice the radius of the first is used. Is this perfectly safe if it is known that the first wire will just safely carry the ball suspended from it?

23. CONICAL SURFACE

Definition. *A conical surface is a surface generated by a moving straight line (generator) which always intersects a fixed plane curve (directrix) and which always passes through a fixed point (vertex) not in the plane of the curve.*

Properties

1. An *element* of a conical surface is the generator in any particular position.

2. Any line, not an element, tangent to any curve on a conical surface is tangent to the surface.

3. A plane is tangent to a conical surface if it contains an element of the conical surface and a line tangent to the surface.

24. CONE

Definition. *A cone is the solid bounded by a conical surface (lateral surface) whose directrix is a closed curve, and a plane (base) which cuts all the elements.*

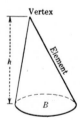

Properties

1. The *altitude* of a cone is the perpendicular distance from the vertex to the plane of the base.

2. Every section of a cone made by a plane passing through its vertex and containing two points of the base is a triangle.

3. The axis of a cone is the straight line joining the vertex with the center of the base (if the base has a center).

4. A *right section* of a cone is a section perpendicular to its axis and cutting all the elements.

5. A circular cone is a cone whose right section is a circle.

Formula

The volume of a cone is equal to one-third the product of the base and the altitude.

$$Volume = \tfrac{1}{3} \, base \times altitude.$$
$$V = \tfrac{1}{3}Bh.$$

Volume analysis. Consider the cone $O\text{–}EFGH$ shown in the figure. Construct the pyramid $O'\text{–}E'F'G'H'$ having a base and altitude respectively equal to the base and altitude of the cone. Place these solids so that their bases lie in the same plane as shown.

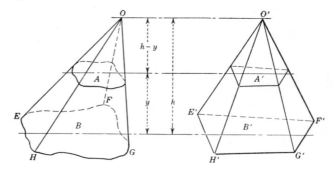

Pass a plane parallel to and distant y from the bases cutting the cone in section A and the pyramid in section A'. Denote the altitude of each solid by h, the base of the cone by B, and the base of the pyramid by B'. From §22, we have

$$\frac{A}{B} = \frac{(h-y)^2}{h^2}$$

and

$$\frac{A'}{B'} = \frac{(h-y)^2}{h^2}.$$

Equating these two values of $\dfrac{(h-y)^2}{h^2}$, we get

$$\frac{A}{B} = \frac{A'}{B'}.$$

But by construction $\qquad B = B'.$

Therefore $\qquad A = A'.$

Since the altitude of each solid is h and since $A = A'$, it follows from Cavalieri's theorem that the volumes of the two solids are equal. But the volume of the pyramid is $\frac{1}{3}B'h = \frac{1}{3}Bh$. Therefore the volume of the cone is $\frac{1}{3}Bh$.

PROBLEMS

1. The crater of a volcano is approximately in the shape of a cone of base 3.1416 sq. mi. The crater's depth is 1500 ft. How many cubic yards of earth would be required to fill this cavity?

2. A stalactite which may be seen hanging in the Endless Caverns in Virginia is approximately in the form of a cone 4 ft. long with a base 18 in. in diameter. The calcium carbonate of which it is formed weighs 131 lb. per cu. ft. Find the weight of the stalactite.

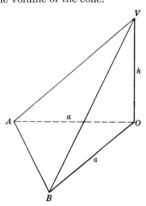

3. A conical pile of sand 6 ft. in height has a volume of 27 cu. ft. If the bottom of the pile is on level ground, how much ground does it cover?

4. The vertex of the cone shown in the figure is at the midpoint of an upper edge of the cube; the base of the cone is a circle inscribed in the lower base of the cube. If the edge of the cube is 12 in., find the volume of the cone.

5. In the triangular pyramid shown in the figure each face angle at O is 90°. Find the volume of a cone whose vertex is at V and whose base is a circle inscribed in the base ABO of the pyramid.

6. At what distance from the vertex of a cone of altitude h must a plane parallel to the base be passed, so as to bisect the lateral surface? At what distance must it be passed so as to bisect the solid?

7. Show that every section of a cone made by a plane passing through its vertex and containing two points of the base is a triangle.

★**8.** Find the face angles at V of the pyramid of Prob. 5.

25. RIGHT CIRCULAR CONE

Definition. *A right circular cone is a circular cone whose axis is perpendicular to its base.*

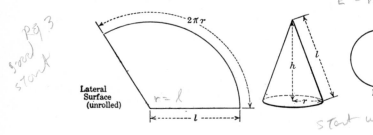

Properties

1. The *slant height* of a right circular cone is the length of an element.

2. The *altitude* of a right circular cone is the distance between the vertex and the center of the circle which forms its base.

3. A right circular cone is a solid generated by rotating a right triangle about one of its legs as an axis; the surface generated by the hypotenuse of the triangle is the lateral area of the cone, and the area of the base of the cone is the surface generated by the leg which is not the axis of rotation.

4. All elements of a right circular cone are equal.

5. A section of a right circular cone parallel to the base is a circle whose center is on the axis of the cone.

6. A section of a right circular cone which contains the vertex and two points of the base is an isosceles triangle.

Formulas

The lateral area of a right circular cone is equal to one-half the product of the circumference of the base and the slant height.

Lateral area = $\frac{1}{2}$ circumference of base $\times$ slant height.
$$S = \tfrac{1}{2}cl.$$

The volume of a right circular cone is equal to one-third the product of the base and the altitude.

Volume = $\frac{1}{3}$ base $\times$ altitude.
$$V = \tfrac{1}{3}Bh.$$

Surface analysis. If the curved surface of a right circular cone be slit along an element and spread out flat as shown in the figure, it becomes a sector of a circle, with an element as radius and the circumference of the cone's base as arc. Therefore by §3, its area is $\frac{1}{2}cl$.

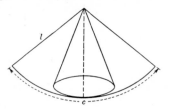

Example 1. Write a formula for the volume V of a right circular cone in terms of the radius of the base r and the altitude h.

Solution. Since the base of the right circular cone is a circle of radius r, its area is $B = \pi r^2$. Substituting this value of B in the formula

$$V = \tfrac{1}{3}Bh,$$

we get

$$V = \tfrac{1}{3}\pi r^2 h. \quad Ans.$$

Example 2. The liquid content of a glass is in the form of a cone of base diameter 3 in. If the glass contains 10 fluid oz., and 1 fluid oz. = 1.805 cu. in., what is the greatest depth of the liquid?

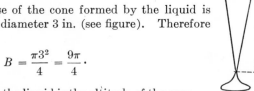

Solution. The base of the cone formed by the liquid is the area of a circle of diameter 3 in. (see figure). Therefore we have

$$B = \frac{\pi 3^2}{4} = \frac{9\pi}{4}.$$

The greatest depth of the liquid is the altitude of the cone.

Substituting $V = (10)\,(1.805)$ cu. in. and $B = \dfrac{9\pi}{4}$ in the formula

$$V = \tfrac{1}{3}Bh,$$

we obtain

$$(10)\,(1.805) = \frac{1}{3}\left(\frac{9\pi}{4}\right)h.$$

Solving this equation for h, we find

$$h = \textbf{7.6606 in.} \quad Ans.$$

Example 3. What is the volume of the right circular cone that can be formed by using as its lateral surface the semicircular area shown in the figure?

Solution. When the given area is rolled into the lateral surface of the right circular cone, the point A becomes the vertex and each radius

of the area becomes an element of the cone as shown in the figure.   Let
the altitude of the cone be h and the radius of the base be r.

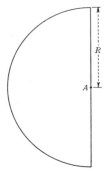

Since the semicircular arc of the given area
forms the circumference of the base of the cone,
we have

$$\pi R = 2\pi r$$

or

$$r = \frac{R}{2} \cdot$$

Therefore each axial section of
the cone is an equilateral triangle,
such as triangle ABC, of altitude
h and base $2r$.   This triangle is
divided into the two equal $30° -$
$60°$ right triangles ABO and ACO by the axis AO.   Therefore

$$h = \frac{1}{2} \sqrt{3}\, R.$$

To find the volume of the cone we substitute $B = \pi r^2 = \pi \left(\dfrac{R}{2}\right)^2 =$
$\dfrac{\pi R^2}{4}$ and $h = \dfrac{\sqrt{3}}{2} R$ in the formula

$$V = \frac{1}{3}Bh$$

and obtain

$$V = \frac{1}{3}\left(\frac{\pi R^2}{4}\right)\left(\frac{\sqrt{3}}{2}\, R\right) = \frac{\sqrt{3}\pi R^3}{24} \cdot \quad Ans.$$

Example 4.   The upper
portion of a sherbet glass is
in the form of a right circular
cone with a base of radius 2
in. and a slant height of 4
in. (inner dimensions).   Find
the volume of liquid it contains (a) when full, (b) when
filled to a depth of 3 in.

Solution. (a) First consider the cone occupied by
the liquid when the glass is
full.   Pass a plane through
the axis OB of the cone,

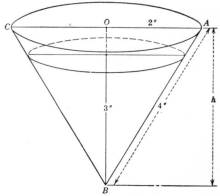

forming the section ABC shown in the figure.   Let $h = OB$ be the
altitude of the cone.   Applying the Pythagorean theorem to right

triangle AOB, we have

$$h = \sqrt{4^2 - 2^2} = 2\sqrt{3}.$$

Denoting the volume of the cone by V_2 and substituting $B = \pi(2)^2 = 4\pi$ and $h = 2\sqrt{3}$ in the formula

$$V = \tfrac{1}{3}Bh,$$

we get

$$V_2 = \tfrac{1}{3}(4\pi)\,(2\sqrt{3}) = \frac{8\pi\sqrt{3}}{3} = \textbf{14.510 cu. in.} \quad Ans.$$

(b) Now consider the cone occupied by the water when the glass is filled to a depth of 3 in. Since this cone is similar to the cone in part (a), we write

$$\frac{V_1}{V_2} = \frac{h_1^3}{h_2^3},$$

where V_1, V_2 and h_1, h_2 are the volumes and altitudes of the two cones, respectively. Substituting $V_2 = \dfrac{8\pi\sqrt{3}}{3}$, $h_1 = 3$, and $h_2 = 2\sqrt{3}$ in this equation, we get

$$\frac{V_1}{\dfrac{8\pi\sqrt{3}}{3}} = \frac{3^3}{(2\sqrt{3})^3}$$

or

$$V_1 = 3\pi = \textbf{9.4248 cu. in.} \quad Ans.$$

PROBLEMS

1. A pile of sand is in the form of a right circular cone of altitude 7 ft. and slant height 25 ft. What is the weight of the sand, if the sand weighs 107.5 lb. per cu. ft.?

2. How many square yards of canvas will be required to make a conical tent 15 ft. high and 18 ft. in diameter, if 10 per cent of the material is wasted?

3. A cylindrical tower 30 ft. in diameter has a conical roof the length of whose eaves is 2 ft. An element of the roof is inclined 45° to the horizontal. Find the weather surface (see figure).

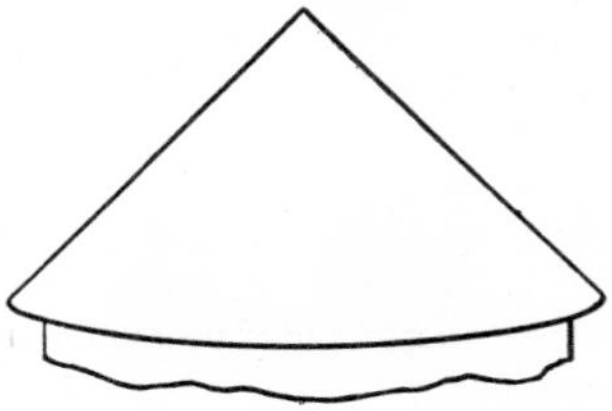

4. Two vertical conical tanks (both inverted) have their vertices connected by a short horizontal pipe. One tank, initially full of water, has an altitude of 6 ft. and a diameter of base 7 ft. The other tank, initially empty, has an altitude of 9 ft. and a diameter of base 8 ft. If the water is allowed to flow through the connecting pipe, find the level to which the water will ultimately rise in the empty tank. (Neglect the water in the pipe.)

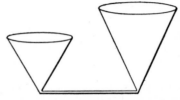

5. A circular piece of filter paper R inches in radius is folded twice: first on a diameter and then on the radius perpendicular to the crease. It is then opened up so as to form a right circular cone. Find in terms of R the volume of liquid it will hold.

6. The solid shown consists of a right circular cylinder of diameter d and altitude h, surmounted by a cone of diameter of base d and altitude $h/2$. (a) Write a formula for the volume. (b) Find the volume, given $d = 4.42$ in. and $h = 5.17$ in.

7. A piece of lead pipe of inner diameter $2\frac{1}{4}$ in., outer diameter $2\frac{5}{8}$ in., and length 16 ft., has been melted in an open conical pot of radius 10 in. and altitude 15 in. Find the depth of the molten metal.

8. A right circular cone of slant height 10 in. has a radius of 4 in. Find the angle of the sector of a circle of radius 10 in. whose area is equal to the lateral area of the cone.

9. A piece of paper in the form of a sector of a circle of radius 12 in. is rolled into a cone. Calculate the volume of the cone if the angle of the sector is (a) 60°, (b) 90°, (c) 180°, (d) 270°, (e) 265°.

★10. Find the vertical angle of each of the cones of Prob. 4.

26. MISCELLANEOUS PROBLEMS

1. The lateral edge of a pyramidal church spire is 61 ft. Each side of its octagonal base is 22 ft. What will be the cost of painting the spire at $2\frac{1}{2}$ cents a square foot?

2. Each element of a circular conical pile of sand 6 ft. high is inclined 45° to the horizontal. How many cubic feet of sand does the pile contain?

3. The inside dimensions of a trunk are 4 ft., 3 ft., 2 ft. Find the dimensions of a trunk similar in shape that will hold 4 times as much.

4. How many square feet of canvas are required for a conical tent 18 ft. high and 10 ft. in diameter if 10 per cent of the material is wasted?

5. A model steamboat is 2 ft. 3 in. long and it displaces 1.5 lb. of water. The ship of which the model is made is 720 ft. long. What is its displacement in tons?

6. Among the interesting applications of similarity is the case of a shadow, as here shown, where the light is the center of similitude.   If a man's profile is 12 in. in height and the similar shadow is 16 in. in height, find the ratio of the area of the profile to the area of the shadow.

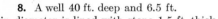

7. How far from the top must you cut a conical tent in order to cut the cloth in half?

8. A well 40 ft. deep and 6.5 ft. in diameter is lined with stone 1.5 ft. thick so that the inner diameter of the well becomes 3.5 ft.   Find the number of cubic feet of stone required.

9. A pyramidal roof 16 ft. in height, standing on a square base 24 ft. on a side, is covered with sheet lead $\frac{1}{16}$ in. thick.   (a) Find the weight of the lead if 1 cu. in. of lead weighs 7 oz.   (b) If the lead is stripped off and cast into bullets, each of which is in the form of a cylinder $\frac{1}{2}$ in. long and $\frac{4}{11}$ in. in diameter, surmounted by a cone of the same diameter and $\frac{3}{8}$ in. high, find how many bullets there will be.

10. The monument erected in Babylon by Queen Semiramis at her husband Ninus's tomb is said to have been one block of solid marble in the form of a square pyramid, the sides of whose base were 20 ft. and the height of the monument 150 ft.   If the marble weighed 185 lb. per cu. ft., find the weight of the monument.

11. Find the volume of the largest pyramid which can be cut from a rectangular parallelepiped whose edges are 2 in. by 3 in. by 4 in.   Discuss fully.

12. Find the least waste in cutting two conical blocks from a block of wood in the form of a right circular cylinder of radius 4 in. and altitude 7 in.

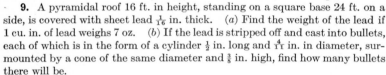

13. A mound of earth in the form of the solid shown in the figure has a rectangular base 17 yd. long and 8.62 yd. wide.   Its perpendicular height is 5 yd., and the length on the top is 8.56 yd.   Find the number of cubic yards of earth in the mound.

14. A vessel is in the form of an inverted regular square pyramid of altitude 9.87 in. and base edge 6.27 in.   The depth of the water it contains is 6 in. (a) How much will the surface rise when 1 pt. of water is added?   (One gal. = 231 cu. in.)   (b) Find the wetted surface when the depth of the water is 9.23 in.

15. Find the volume of the largest cone having its circular base circumscribed about a face of a rectangular parallelepiped of dimensions 2 ft. by 3 ft. by 4 ft. and its vertex lying in the opposite face.

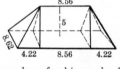

16. An ink bottle is in the form of a right circular cylinder with a large conical opening as shown in the figure. When it is filled level with the bottom of the opening, it can just be turned upside down without any ink spilling. Prove that the depth of the cone is three-fifths the depth of the bottle.

17. Three of the edges of a rectangular parallelepiped that meet in a point are also the lateral edges of a pyramid.   What fraction of the parallelepiped is this pyramid?

18. Pass a plane containing a vertex of a rectangular parallelepiped and a diagonal of a face not containing that vertex to cut a pyramid from the parallelepiped.   What fraction of the volume of the parallelepiped is the volume of the pyramid thus cut off?

19. A pyramid is cut by a plane parallel to the base and bisecting the altitude.   What fraction of the entire pyramid is the smaller pyramid cut away by this plane?

20. A wooden cone of altitude h is to be sawed into three parts of equal weight.   How far from the vertex must the cuts (parallel to the base) be made?

21. A right circular cylinder is inscribed in a right circular cone of altitude h and radius of base x, as shown in the figure.   Find the radius of the cylinder if its lateral area is equal to the lateral area of the small cone which surmounts the cylinder.

22. Solve Prob. 21 if the lateral area of the small cone is equal to the area of the ring bounded by the circumferences of the base of the large cone and the lower base of the cylinder.

23. Upon the faces of a cube as bases congruent regular pyramids are constructed exterior to the cube.   If an edge of the cube is 6 in. and if the distances between the vertices of the two opposite pyramids is 10 in., find the surface of the resulting solid.

24. The cube shown in the figure is cut by two planes, one passing through vertex A and containing edge ED, the other passing through the same vertex A and containing edge EB.   Find the volume and total area of the pyramid whose base is $BCDE$ and whose vertex is A if $AC = a$.

25. Pass a plane through a cube of edge 8 in. so that the section formed will be a regular hexagon.   Through each side of the hexagon pass two planes, one plane containing one of the two vertices of the cube which are farthest away from the plane of the hexagon, the other plane containing the diagonally opposite vertex of the cube.   Find the volume of the solid bounded by these planes.

★26. A and B are diametrically opposite points on the base of a cone of semivertical angle 35°, slant height 6 in.   Find the difference between the distance of B from A measured around the rim of the base and the distance of B from A measured along the shortest path across the curved surface of the cone.

Hint.   Unroll the curved surface.

CHAPTER V

SOLIDS FOR WHICH $V = (\text{mean } B)h$.

27. INTRODUCTION

We shall now consider another class of solids each of whose volumes is the product of its mean base and its altitude.

28. FRUSTUM OF REGULAR PYRAMID

Definition. *A frustum of a regular pyramid is the portion of a regular pyramid included between the base and a section parallel to the base.*

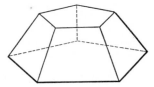

Properties

1. The *slant height* of a frustum of a regular pyramid is the altitude of a face.

2. The lateral edges of a frustum of a regular pyramid are equal, and the faces are equal isosceles trapezoids.

Formulas

The lateral area of the frustum of a **regular** pyramid is equal to one-half the sum of the perimeters of the bases multiplied by the slant height.

$$Lateral\ area = \frac{sum\ of\ perimeters\ of\ bases}{2} \times slant\ height$$

$$S = \text{mean } p \times l.$$

$$S = \frac{(p + P)l}{2}.$$

The volume of the frustum of **any** pyramid is equal to one-third the product of the altitude and the sum of the upper base, the lower base, and the mean proportional between the bases.

$$Volume = \frac{sum\ of\ bases\ +\ mean\ proportional}{3} \times altitude.$$

$$V = \text{mean } B \times h.$$

$$V = \frac{(b + B + \sqrt{bB})}{3}\, h.$$

Surface analysis.   The area of the lateral surface of a frustum of a pyramid is the sum of the areas of the trapezoidal faces.

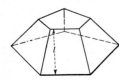

In the frustum of a regular pyramid (see figure) let S be the lateral surface, let l be the slant height, and let p and P be the perimeters of the bases.   The lateral faces are equal isosceles trapezoids with common altitude l.   Therefore the area of the sum of the faces $= S = \frac{1}{2}$(common altitude) (sum of perimeters of the bases), or in symbols

$$S = \tfrac{1}{2}l(p + P).$$

Volume analysis.   Consider the frustum of **any** pyramid $C'F$ shown in the figure.   Denote the volume by V, the area of the lower base by B, the area of the upper base by b, and the altitude by h.   Complete the pyramid $O–CDFG$ of which the frustum $C'F$ is a part.   Draw OE perpendicular to base B, cutting base b at E'.   Then $h = EE'$.   Denote $E'O$ by H.

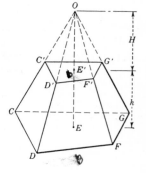

Referring to the figure, we write

Volume $C'F =$ volume $O–CDFG -$
            volume $O–C'D'F'G'$;

or in terms of the dimensions, we write

$$V = \tfrac{1}{3}B(h + H) - \tfrac{1}{3}bH.$$

or

$$V = \tfrac{1}{3}[Bh + (B - b)H]. \qquad (1)$$

By §22, we have

$$\frac{b}{B} = \frac{H^2}{(H + h)^2}.$$

Solving this equation for H, we find

$$H = \frac{h \sqrt{b}}{\sqrt{B} - \sqrt{b}}.$$

Substituting in (1) this value of H, we get

$$V = \frac{1}{3}\left[Bh + (B - b)\frac{h \sqrt{b}}{\sqrt{B} - \sqrt{b}}\right].$$

Simplifying, we have

$$V = \frac{[B + b + \sqrt{Bb}]}{3} h.$$

Example.   The lower portion of the Washington monument was built before the Civil War.   This portion is in the shape of a frustum of a square pyramid.   The altitude of the frustum is 150 ft., and its lower base measures 55 ft. on a side as shown in the figure.   The faces of the monument slope inward 0.247 in. horizontally in a vertical rise of 1 ft.   The structure is hollowed out along its entire length by a vertical shaft which has a uniform square cross section 25 ft. on a side.   Find how much stone was used in its construction.

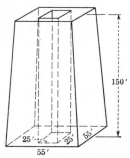

Solution.   In the figure is shown an axial section of the structure made by a plane passed through the axis of

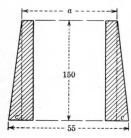

the solid and perpendicular to a pair of opposite base edges.   If we let $2c$ be the difference between the edges of the upper and lower bases and a be the length of the edge of the upper base, we write

$$2c = 55 - a \qquad (a)$$

Since the monument slopes inward 0.247 in. horizontally to a rise of 1 ft. vertically, we have

$$c = \left(\frac{0.247}{12}\right)(150) = 3.0875 \text{ ft.}$$

Solving equation (a) for a and substituting $c = 3.0875$, we obtain

$$a = 55 - 2c = 55 - 2(3.0875) = 48.825.$$

Since the upper and lower bases of the frustum are squares, we find their areas to be respectively

$$b = a^2 = (48.825)^2$$

and

$$B = (55)^2.$$

Substituting $b = (48.825)^2$, $B = (55)^2$, and $h = 150$ in the formula

$$V = \frac{(b + B + \sqrt{bB})}{3} h,$$

we find the volume of the frustum to be

$$V = \left[\frac{(48.825)^2 + (55)^2 + (55)\,(48.825)}{3} \right] 150 = 404{,}710 \text{ cu. ft.}$$

The shaft of the structure is in the form of a rectangular parallelepiped of altitude $h = 150$ and area of base $B = (25)^2$. Substituting $V = V_1$, $B = (25)^2$, and $h = 150$ in the formula

$$V = Bh,$$

we get

$$V_1 = (25)^2\,(150) = 93{,}750 \text{ cu. ft.}$$

Therefore the amount of stone used in the construction is

$$V - V_1 = 404{,}710 - 93{,}750 = \textbf{310,960 cu. ft.} \quad Ans.$$

PROBLEMS $1 - 6$

1. A berry box, sold to contain a quart of berries, is in the form of the frustum of a pyramid 5 in. square at the top, $4\frac{1}{2}$ in. square at the bottom, and $2\frac{7}{8}$ in. deep. A U. S. dry quart contains 67.2 cu. in. How does the capacity of the box compare with this standard measure?

2. Find the depth of a hopper to hold 15 bu. of grain, if it is to be built in the shape of the frustum of a square pyramid with the upper and lower bases measuring 7 and 4 ft. on a side, respectively. (A bushel = $1\frac{1}{4}$ cu. ft.)

3. Cleopatra's Needle (the Egyptian Obelisk in New York) consists of a frustum of a pyramid surmounted by a pyramid. The frustum has square bases. The upper base measures 4 ft. on a side and the lower base measures $7\frac{1}{2}$ ft. on a side. The altitude of the frustum is 61 ft. Find the weight of the frustum, if it is made of stone which weighs 170 lb. per cu. ft.

4. How many cubic yards of earth must be removed in digging an artificial lake 15 ft. deep, if the level bottom is a rectangle 180 ft. by 20 ft. and the top is a rectangle 216 ft. by 24 ft.?

5. A baking pan has a rectangular base 12 in. by 8 in.; the sides and ends of the pan slope outward, so that the upper edges measure respectively $13\frac{1}{2}$ in. by 9 in. If the depth of the pan is 2 in., find the amount of cake batter required to fill the pan to one-half its depth.

6. The army squad tent shown in the figure has a roof with trapezoidal sides whose bases form a rectangle $1\frac{3}{4}$ ft. by 2 ft. at the top and a rectangle 14 ft. by 16 ft. at the bottom. If the height of the roof is 8 ft., find the surface area of canvas in the roof. (Neglect the rounded surface at the top and the entrance opening.)

7. A regular square pyramid has a base whose area is 25 sq. in. A section parallel to the base and 3.18 in. above it has an area of 4 sq. in. Find the ratio of the volume of the frustum to the volume of the pyramid.

8. The flowerpot shown in the sketch has a uniform thickness of 3 in. and is 1 ft. high. Find the amount of material necessary to construct 1000 such pots. (Neglect the drain in the bottom.)

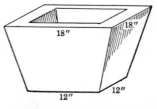

★9. A block of granite is in the form of the frustum of a regular square pyramid whose upper and lower base edges are 3 ft. and 7 ft., respectively. If each of the lateral faces is inclined at an angle of 62° 30′ to the base, find the volume of granite in the block.

29. FRUSTUM OF RIGHT CIRCULAR CONE

Definition. *The frustum of a right circular cone is that portion of a right circular cone included between the base and a section parallel to the base.*

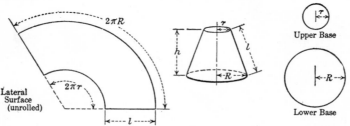

Properties

1. The altitude of a frustum of a right circular cone is the perpendicular distance between the two bases.

2. All the elements of a frustum of a right circular cone are equal.

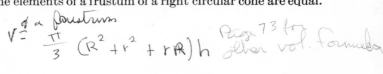

$V =$ of a frustum

$$V = \frac{\pi}{3}(R^2 + r^2 + rR)h \qquad \text{Page 73 for other vol. formulas}$$

Formulas

The lateral area of the frustum of a right circular cone is equal to one-half the sum of the circumferences of the bases multiplied by the slant height.

Lateral area = ½ sum of circumferences of bases × slant height.

$$S = \text{mean } c \times l.$$

$$S = \frac{c + C}{2} l.$$

The volume of the frustum of any cone is equal to one-third of the product of the altitude and the sum of the upper base, the lower base, and the mean proportional between the two bases.

$$Volume = \frac{sum\ of\ bases + mean\ proportional}{3} \times altitude.$$

$$V = \text{mean } B \times h.$$

$$V = \frac{(b + B + \sqrt{bB})}{3} h.$$

Surface analysis. If we complete the cone of the frustum of a 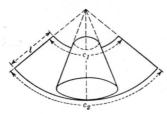 right circular cone and if we slit it along an element as shown in the figure, the curved surface of the frustum develops (unrolls) into the difference of two similar sectors having a common angle, the arcs of the sectors being the circumferences of the bases of the frustum. Denoting the radii of these arcs by r and $r + l$ and using the formula for the area of a sector (from §3), we write

$$S = \tfrac{1}{2}(r + l)c_2 - \tfrac{1}{2}rc_1 = \tfrac{1}{2}[r(c_2 - c_1) + lc_2]. \qquad (a)$$

But from Reference 67, §50, we have

$$\frac{c_1}{c_2} = \frac{r}{r + l},$$

or

$$r(c_2 - c_1) = lc_1.$$

Substituting this value of $r(c_2 - c_1)$ in (a), we obtain

$$S = \tfrac{1}{2}l(c_1 + c_2).$$

Volume analysis. Consider the frustum ET of a cone shown in the figure. Denote the volume by V, the area of the lower base by B, the area of the upper base by b, and the altitude by h. Complete the cone O–$RSTU$ of which frustum ET is a part. Construct the pyramid O'–$R'S'T'U'$ having its base and altitude respectively equal to the base and altitude of the cone. Place the solids so that their bases lie in the same plane as shown. Pass a plane containing b and intersecting the pyramid in section b', forming the frustum $E'T'$. From §24, $b = b'$.

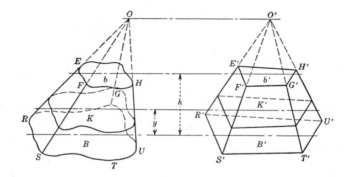

Pass a second plane parallel to and distant y from the bases of the frustums cutting the solids in sections K and K', respectively. Since, from §24, $K = K'$, and since the altitude of each frustum is h, it follows from Cavalieri's theorem that the volumes of the two solids are equal. But from §28 the volume of the frustum $E'T'$ is

$$V = \frac{(b + B + \sqrt{bB})}{3}\,h.$$

Hence the volume of ET is

$$V = \frac{(b + B + \sqrt{bB})}{3}\,h.$$

Example. A reservoir contains 54,000,000 gal. of water when full. Find the depth of the water if the reservoir is in the form of the frustum of a right circular cone of upper and lower base radii 200 ft. and 100 ft., respectively.

Solution. The areas of the lower and upper bases b and B (see figure) are respectively $\pi(100)^2$ and $\pi(200)^2$. Denoting the depth of the water by h, we write for its volume

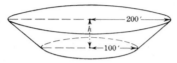

$$V = \left(\frac{b + B + \sqrt{bB}}{3}\right)h,$$

or

$$V = \frac{\pi(100)^2 + \pi(200)^2 + \pi(100)\ (200)}{3}\,h = \tfrac{1}{3}(100)^2\pi(7)h. \qquad (a)$$

But we are given that

$$V = 54,000,000 \text{ gal.} = \frac{54,000,000(231)}{1728} \text{ cu. ft.} \qquad (b)$$

Equating the values of V from (a) and (b), we have

$$\frac{54,000,000(231)}{1728} = \tfrac{1}{3}(100)^2\pi(7)h,$$

from which we find

$$h = \textbf{98.475 ft.}\quad Ans.$$

PROBLEMS

1. Show that the formula for the volume of a pyramid (cone) can be derived from the formula for the volume of a frustum of a pyramid (cone) if one base of the frustum becomes a point. Show also that the volume of a prism (cylinder) can be derived from the volume of the frustum of a pyramid (cone) if one base of the frustum becomes equal to the other base.

2. An 80-ft. flagpole has upper and lower diameters of 4 and 16 in., respectively. Find the cost of painting it at 10 cents per square foot.

3. The inside diameters of the bases of a flowerpot are 10 in. and 7 in., and the slant height is 9 in. How many cubic inches of earth does it contain when it is completely filled?

4. A lamp shade is in the form of a frustum of a cone with slant height 7 in., radii of bases 3 in. and 7 in. respectively. How much material is used in its construction if $\frac{1}{4}$ in. is allowed for the seam?

5. A water pail 12 in. high is in the form of a frustum of a cone. If the diameters of the bases are 10 in. and 12 in. respectively, find its capacity in pints. (One gal. = 231 cu. in.)

6. Find the expense, at 60 cents a square foot, of polishing the curved surface of a marble column in the shape of the frustum of a right circular cone whose slant height is 12 ft. and the radii of whose bases are 3 ft. 6 in., and 2 ft. 4 in., respectively.

7. The chimney of a factory is constructed of brick and is surfaced on the inside with a heat-resisting mortar. The inner and outer diameters at the bottom are 3 ft. and 8 ft., respectively. The chimney tapers uniformly both inside and out, so that at the top the respective diameters are 2.5 ft. and 4 ft. If the height of the chimney is 40 ft., find the amount of material used in its construction and in addition find the surface area exposed to the weather.

8. A manufacturer has an order for 20,000 megaphones. The megaphones, conical in shape, are to be 2 in. in diameter at the smaller end, 8 in. in diameter at the other end, and 1 ft. long. If 10 per cent of the material used in manufacturing them will be wasted, how much material should be ordered?

9. Nozzles may be used as water-measuring devices the same as standard orifices, and are especially useful for that purpose when high heads are employed. They may also be used to furnish jets at high velocities for fire purposes, for power, or for hydraulic mining and similar work. A nozzle which is attached to the end of a 4-in. fire hose has a length of 1 ft. and a diameter at the discharge end of 1 in. If it has a uniform thickness of $\frac{5}{16}$ in. and is made of brass, find the weight of material used in the manufacture of 1000 such nozzles. (Brass weighs 520 lb. per cu. ft.)

10. At what distance from the base of a right circular cone must a plane be passed parallel to the base in order that the volume of the frustum formed shall be three-fifths of the volume of the given cone?

11. Through a given cone, altitude h and base B, two planes are passed parallel to the base, cutting the altitude $h/3$ and $\frac{2}{3}h$ units from the base. Find the ratio of the volumes of the two frustums thus formed.

12. The frustum of a right circular cone has a slant height of 9 ft., and the radii of the bases are 5 ft. and 7 ft. Find the lateral area and the total area. What is the altitude of this frustum? Find the altitude of the cone that was removed to leave this frustum. Also find in two ways the volume of the frustum.

★13. In Prob. 4 find the angle an element makes with the larger base of the frustum.

30. PRISMATOID

Definition. *A prismatoid is a polyhedron having for bases two polygons in parallel planes, and for lateral faces triangles or trape-*

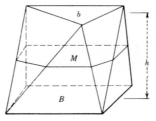

zoids with one side lying in one base, and the opposite vertex or side lying in the other base, of the polyhedron.

Properties

1. The altitude of a prismatoid is the perpendicular distance between the planes of the bases.

2. The mid-section of a prismatoid is the section parallel to the bases and midway between them.

Formulas

The volume of a prismatoid equals the product of one-sixth the sum of the upper base, the lower base, and four times the mid-section by the altitude.

$$Volume = \frac{sum\ of\ bases + 4 \times mid\text{-}section}{6} \times altitude.$$

$$Volume = \text{mean } B^* \times h.$$

$$V = \left[\frac{b + B + 4M}{6} \right] h.$$

NOTE. The foregoing formula is valid for a much more extensive class of solids than prismatoids. (See §§43, 44, 45.) Among these solids are included cones, cylinders, and spheres. In fact, the class of solids whose volume can be found by means of it is so extensive that the formula finds wide practical application. The formula was first stated by Newton in 1711 and first published by James Sterling in his " Methodus Differentialis " in 1730.

Volume analysis. Given the prismatoid GL, shown in the figure, in which the upper base, the lower base, the mid-section,

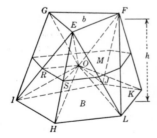

and the altitude are denoted by b, B, M, and h, respectively.

Join any point in the mid-section, as O, with the various vertices of the mid-section and of both bases by the lines OR, OF, OE, etc. Pass planes through these lines dividing the solid into pyramids two of which (O–EFG, O–$HIJKL$) have a common vertex at O, and have as bases b and B respectively, and each of the others (such as O–EIH) has as base one of the lateral faces of the prismatoid. The volumes of these pyramids are found separately.

* This is a weighted mean.

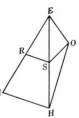

(a) Volume $O\text{–}EFG = \frac{1}{3}(b)\left(\frac{h}{2}\right) = \frac{hb}{6}.$

(b) Volume $O\text{–}HIJKL = \frac{1}{3}(B)\left(\frac{h}{2}\right) = \frac{hB}{6}.$

(c) Volume $O\text{–}EIH$ is divided into two parts by the mid-section. Since RS joins the midpoints of the sides of EIH,

$$ERS = \tfrac{1}{4}EIH, \text{ and volume } O\text{–}ERS = \tfrac{1}{4}O\text{–}EIH.$$

But $O\text{–}ERS = E\text{–}ORS = \frac{1}{3}(ORS)(\frac{1}{2}h) = \dfrac{h}{6}(ORS).$

Therefore volume $O\text{–}EIH = 4(O\text{–}ERS) = 4 \cdot \dfrac{h}{6} \cdot ORS.$

In a similar manner the volume of each of the remaining portions of the figure not considered under (a) and (b) can be shown to be equal to $4 \cdot \dfrac{h}{6}$ times the area of the mid-section included in it.

Hence, by adding together the portions of the prismatoid not considered in (a) and (b), we find their volume to be $4 \cdot \dfrac{h}{6} \cdot M.$

Adding the volumes found in (a), (b), and this last result, we get $V = \dfrac{(b + B + 4M)}{6}\,h.$ This is known as the *prismoidal formula*.

Example. A certain quartz crystal with plane surfaces has the dimensions shown in the figure. If the upper and lower bases lie in parallel planes, find the volume of the crystal.

Solution. The crystal is in the form of a prismatoid. To form the mid-section pass a plane parallel to and equidistant from the two bases. This section $ABCDE$ is shown in the sketch of the solid and again in the plane of the paper.

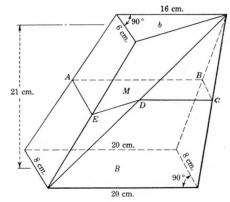

Since the bases and mid-section of the solid are parallel, the plane of the mid-section intersects each face in a line parallel to the base of this face, since the mid-section is equidistant from the bases of the solid, it bisects each edge.   Therefore, considering the triangular faces (see figure), we find

$$DC = \tfrac{1}{2}(20) = 10$$

and $BC = \tfrac{1}{2}(8) = 4.$

From the trapezoidal faces, we have

$$AE = \tfrac{1}{2}(6 + 8) = 7$$

and

$$AB = \tfrac{1}{2}(16 + 20) = 18.$$

From the figure we see that the area of the mid-section M is the area of the rectangle $ABCF$ plus the area of the triangle EDF.   Hence

$$M = (4)\,(18) + \tfrac{1}{2}(8)\,(3) = 84.$$

The area of the triangular upper base b of the prismatoid is

$$b = \tfrac{1}{2}(16)\,(6) = 48,$$

and the area of the rectangular lower base B is

$$B = (8)\,(20) = 160.$$

Substituting $h = 21, b = 48, B = 160,$ and $M = 84$ in the formula

$$V = \frac{(b + B + 4M)}{6}\,h.$$

we get

$$V = \left[\frac{48 + 160 + 4(84)}{6}\right]21 = \textbf{1904 c.c.}\quad Ans.$$

PROBLEMS

1. In a certain building operation, it was necessary to remove a portion of a hill which was approximately in the shape shown in the sketch.   Lower base is a rectangle; upper base is a right triangle. AB is parallel to DE; and AC is parallel to DG. All face angles at A and at D are right angles.   Altitude of solid is $AD = 240$ ft.; other dimensions are shown in the sketch. Find the amount of earth removed.

2. A railway embankment across a valley has the following dimensions: width at top, 24 ft.; width at base, 66 ft.; height, 14 ft.; length at top, 286 ft.; length at base, 210 ft.   Find its volume.

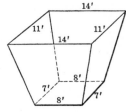

3. The altitude of the storage bin shown in the sketch is 12 ft. and the bases are parallel rectangles having the dimensions indicated. Find the capacity. Is this solid a frustum of a pyramid?

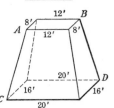

4. The bases (AB and CD) of the granite block shown in the sketch lie in parallel planes; the 12- and 20-ft. edges are parallel; also the 8- and 16-ft. edges are parallel. Find the altitude of the block, if its volume is 4736 cu. ft. The bases AB and CD are rectangular.

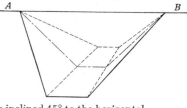

5. The direction of a railroad cut is perpendicular to the horizontal ridge AB. Assuming the sides of the ridge to be plane surfaces making equal angles with the horizontal, find the amount of earth removed if the base is a rectangle, 30 ft. wide by 400 ft. long, in a plane 60 ft. below the line AB; and the sides of the cut are inclined 45° to the horizontal.

6. A pile of ore has a rectangular base 60 ft. wide and 500 ft. long. If the sides of the pile are all inclined 45° to the horizontal, and the ore weighs 110 lb. per cu. ft., find the number of tons of ore in the pile.

7. The railroad fill shown in the figure has sloping sides which rise vertically $\frac{1}{2}$ ft. for each foot horizontally. The top of the fill $ABCD$ is horizontal and the ends are vertical. The depth of the fill at each of the points A, B, C, D is indicated in the figure. Find the cost of making this fill at 75 cents per cubic yard.

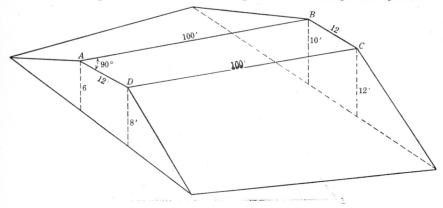

8. The railroad cut shown in the figure has sides inclined at 45° to the hori-

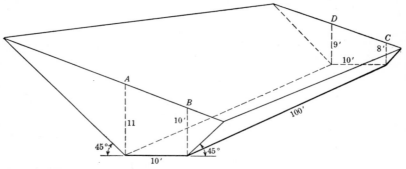

zontal.   The base of the cut is a horizontal rectangle, and the ends are vertical. The depth of the cut at each of the points A, B, C, D is indicated in the figure. Find the cost of making the cut at $1 per cubic yard.

9. Given the prismoidal formula, derive the formula for the frustum of a pyramid.

★**10.** Solve Prob. 8 if the sides of the cut are inclined 26°30' to the horizontal.

★**11.** The block of granite shown in the figure has as lower base the horizontal triangle CDE.   The upper edge AB is horizontal and point D lies in the plane ABC. Find the volume.

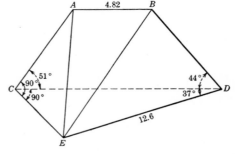

★**12.** In the solid shown below each face angle at A and B is 90°, $AB = 9'$, vertex E lies in the plane CAD, and edges DE and AC are parallel.   Find the volume of the solid.

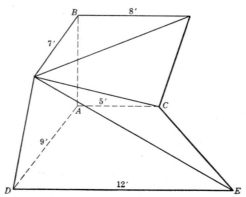

31. TRUNCATED PRISM (OR CYLINDER)

Definition. *A truncated prism (or cylinder) is the portion of a prism (or cylinder) included between the base and a plane not parallel to the base cutting all the edges (or elements).*

A *right truncated prism* (or *cylinder*) is one in which a right section is parallel to the base.

Formula

The volume of a truncated triangular prism is equal to the product of a right section and one-third the sum of the lateral edges.

Volume = right section × average lateral edge

$$V = Km$$

$$V = K\left(\frac{e_1 + e_2 + e_3}{3}\right),$$

where e_1, e_2, and e_3 denote the lateral edges.

The volume of any truncated prism may be obtained by dividing the given truncated prism into truncated triangular prisms.

Example. The truncated prism shown in the figure may be considered as a right prism

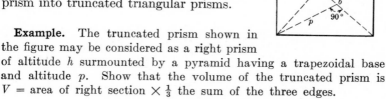

of altitude h surmounted by a pyramid having a trapezoidal base and altitude p. Show that the volume of the truncated prism is V = area of right section × $\frac{1}{3}$ the sum of the three edges.

Solution.   Volume = volume of right prism + volume of pyramid

$$= \tfrac{1}{2}pbh + \tfrac{1}{2}(d_1 + d_2)\ (b)\left(\frac{p}{3}\right)$$

$$= \tfrac{1}{2}pb\left(h + \frac{d_1 + d_2}{3}\right)$$

$$= \tfrac{1}{2}pb(3h + d_1 + d_2)\tfrac{1}{3}$$

$$= \tfrac{1}{2}pb[h + (h + d_1) + (h + d_2)]\tfrac{1}{3}$$

$$= \tfrac{1}{2}pb\left(\frac{e_1 + e_2 + e_3}{3}\right) = K\left(\frac{e_1 + e_2 + e_3}{3}\right).\ Ans.$$

PROBLEMS

1. If each face angle at B is 90°, find the volume of the truncated prism shown in Fig.(a).

2. The solid shown in Fig.(b) is the frustum of a regular square pyramid of altitude 4 in.   Point A is the midpoint of the line joining the midpoints of the parallel sides of face CD.   If a right circular cylinder of radius 1 in. with its axis perpendicular to face CD at A is passed through the frustum, find the volume cut away.

Hint.   The volume cut away is a truncated cylinder which may be considered a cylinder surmounted by one-half another cylinder.

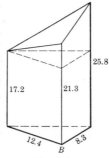

FIG.(a)

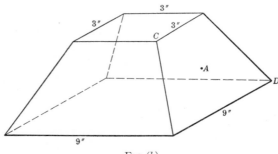

FIG.(b)

3. Show that the volume of a truncated prism whose right section is a parallelogram is the product of its base and its average altitude, or, in terms of the notation in Fig.(c)

$$V = A\left(\frac{h_1 + h_2 + h_3 + h_4}{4}\right).$$

Hint. The prism can be divided into two truncated triangular prisms in two ways (see figure). Apply the formula of the example to each pair, and add the results thus obtained. The sum will be twice the volume of the given prism.

4. Fig.(*d*) represents a truncated triangular prism. Angle

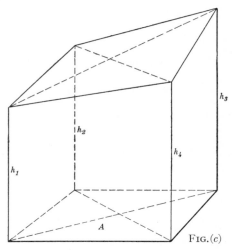

Fig.(*c*)

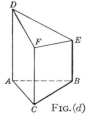

C   Fig.(*d*)

$BAC = 90°$. The lateral edges AD, BE, CF are perpendicular to the base ABC. If $AB = 8$ in., $AC = 6$ in., $AD = 10$ in., $BE = 6$ in., $CF = 8$ in., find: (*a*) the lateral area; (*b*) the total area; (*c*) the volume; ★(*d*) angle EDF; ★(*e*) the angle ABF; ★(*f*) the area of triangle ABF.

32. MISCELLANEOUS PROBLEMS

1. A Dutch windmill in the shape of the frustum of a right circular cone is 12 meters high. The outer diameters at the bottom and the top are 16 meters and 12 meters, the inner diameters 12 meters and 10 meters. How many cubic meters of stone were required to build it?

2. An irregular pile of coal with plane faces is 16 ft. high and covers 600 sq. ft. of level ground. Its mid-section and level top are estimated to contain 400 and 200 sq. ft., respectively. Find the cost of transporting it at $.75 per load, if the coal truck holds 110 cu. ft. of coal.

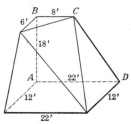

3. Find the volume of the block of earth shown in the sketch. The upper base is a right triangle; the lower base is a rectangle. All face angles at A and B are right angles. The altitude AB is 18 ft. The edges BC and AD are parallel, and all the faces are planes.

4. A railway embankment across a valley has the following dimensions: width at top, 20 ft.; width at base, 45 ft.; height, 11 ft.; length at top, 1020 yd.; length at base, 960 yd. Find its volume.

5. A chimney in the shape of a frustum of a regular pyramid is 186.3 ft. high. Its upper base is a square 10 ft. on a side, and its lower base is a square 16 ft. on a side. The flue is of uniform square cross section, $7\frac{1}{4}$ by $7\frac{1}{4}$ ft. Find the weight of the chimney if the material weighs 112.8 lb. per cu. ft.

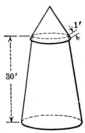

6. A lighthouse consists of a tall tapering tower constructed of brick and has a circular cross section. The tower is surmounted by a conical top consisting of a tin roof with an overhang such that the eave is 1 ft. The overall height of the lighthouse is 40 ft. and the height of the tower 30 ft. Find the area of the brick surface if the lower base of the tower is 20 ft. in diameter and the upper base 12 ft. in diameter. Also find the amount of roofing material used in its construction.

7. An irregular pile of earth is 15 ft. high and covers 500 sq. ft. Its mid-section and level top are estimated to contain 400 and 200 sq. ft., respectively. Find the cost of removing it at 60 cents per load, if the truck measures 3 by 4 by 9 ft.

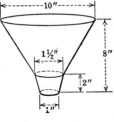

8. How many cubic feet of metal are required to make 1000 funnels such as the one shown in the sketch? The metal used is $\frac{1}{64}$ in. thick. (Neglect seams, waste, etc.)

9. Find the total area of the frustum of a regular square pyramid which is inscribed in the frustum of a cone whose upper and lower base diameters are 4 ft. and 6 ft., respectively, and whose altitude is 12 ft.

10. Bunker Hill Monument is a stone structure in the form of the frustum of a regular square pyramid whose height is 220 ft. and whose base edges are 15 ft. and 30 ft., respectively. Through the center of the monument is a cylindrical opening 11 ft. in diameter at the top and 15 ft. in diameter at the bottom. Find the volume of stone in the monument.

11. An excavation is 12 ft. deep and has trapezoidal sides (faces). The upper base is a horizontal rectangle 400 ft. by 180 ft., and the lower base is a horizontal rectangle 350 ft. by 150 ft. How many cubic yards of earth were removed in digging the excavation?

12. Find the volume and total area of a regular square pyramid which is circumscribed about a frustum of a right

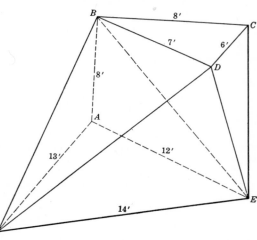

circular cone whose upper and lower base diameters are 7 ft. and 9 ft., respectively, and whose height is 5 ft.

13. In the solid shown on page 84, edge AB is perpendicular to the bases BDC and AEF. Find the volume of the solid, if BD is parallel to AE.

14. The earth removed from a trench 8 ft. deep, 14 ft. wide at the top, and 10 ft. wide at the bottom is thrown up alongside the trench so as to form a bank sloping on each side at the same angle to the horizontal. If the height of the bank is three-fourths the width of its base, find the height of the bank.

15. A block similar to the one considered in Prob. 3 has a volume of 2000 cu. ft. Find its altitude.

16. The space occupied by the water in a reservoir is the frustum of a right circular cone. Each axial section of this frustum has an area of 8800 sq. ft., and the diameters of the upper and the lower bases are in the ratio 6:5. If the reservoir contains 13,600,000 gal., find the depth of the water.

17. The cube shown in the figure measures 3 in. on an edge. Each of the points A, B, C, D is distant 1 in. from the vertex nearest it. Pass planes through (a) point A and edge KN, (b) point B and edge LM, (c) point C and edge KL, (d) point D and edge MN. Find the volume of the largest solid cut from the cube by these planes.

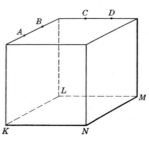

18. Find the difference between the volume of the frustum of a square pyramid whose lower and upper base edges are 8 and 6 ft., respectively, and the volume of a prism of the same altitude whose base is a mid-section of the frustum.

19. Given the frustum of a pyramid of altitude h and lower base B. Find the volume of a pyramid having as base the lower base of the frustum and having its vertex lying in the plane of the upper base of the frustum.

20. The cubical block shown in the figure is 4 in. on an edge. Cut off the corner with vertex G by sawing along the plane determined by points A, B, and E; cut off the part with vertex H by sawing along the plane determined by points A, D, and F; cut off the corner with vertex I by sawing along the plane determined by points C, E, and F; cut the remaining solid into two parts by sawing along the plane determined by points A, E, and F, and find the volume of the larger of these two parts.

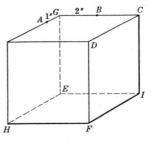

21. If in the frustum of a cone the diameter of the upper base equals the slant height, find the lateral area (a) if the altitude is 4 in. and the perimeter of a vertical section through the axis is 26 in.; (b) if the altitude is 7.2 in. and the perimeter is 39.2 in.

22. Given the prismoidal formula, derive the formula for each of the following solids: cylinder, cone, pyramid, frustum of a right circular cone.

23. The frustum of a regular square pyramid is shown on page 86. Find the area of the section of the frustum formed by a plane containing points

(a) *E, A,* and *C*; (b) *A, C,* and *H*; (c) *A, D,* and *F*; (d) *E, G,* and *D*; (e) *A, G,* and *H*.

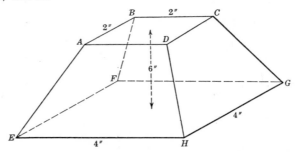

★**24.** The bases of the frustum of a right circular cone are 6 ft. apart and have diameters 5 ft. and 8 ft.   Find (a) the volume of the frustum, (b) the vertical angle of the cone of which the frustum is a part, (c) the area of the lateral surface of the frustum.

CHAPTER VI

THE SPHERE

33. SPHERE

Definition. *A sphere is a solid bounded by a closed surface every point of which is equidistant from a fixed point called the center.*

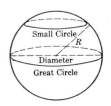

Properties

1. Every plane section of a sphere is a *circle*. If the plane contains a diameter of the sphere, the section is a *great circle*; otherwise, the section is a *small circle*.

2. The *axis of a circle* of a sphere is the diameter of the sphere perpendicular to the plane of the circle.

3. The *poles of a circle* of a sphere are the ends of its axis.

4. Of two circles cut from a sphere by planes unequally distant from the center, the nearer is the greater.

5. The radius of a great circle is equal to the radius of the sphere.

6. Two great circles of a sphere bisect each other.

7. All great circles of a sphere are equal.

8. Every great circle bisects the sphere.

9. The intersection of two spherical surfaces is a circle whose plane is perpendicular to the line joining the centers of the surfaces and whose center is on that line.

10. A plane perpendicular to a radius at its extremity is *tangent* to the sphere.

11. The shortest line that can be drawn on the surface of a sphere between two points is the shorter arc of the great circle passing through them.

Formulas

The area of the surface of a sphere is equal to the area of four of its great circles.

$$Area = area\ of\ 4\ great\ circles.$$
$$S = 4\pi R^2.$$

The volume of a sphere is equal to $\tfrac{4}{3}\pi$ times the cube of its radius.

$$Volume = \tfrac{4}{3}\pi\ (radius)^3.$$
$$V = \tfrac{4}{3}\pi R^3.$$

Surface analysis. Consider the hemisphere cut from the sphere of center O and radius R. Pass two planes distant y apart and parallel to the base of the hemisphere, cutting the hemisphere in two small circles of radii r_1 and r_2 as shown in the figure. If we

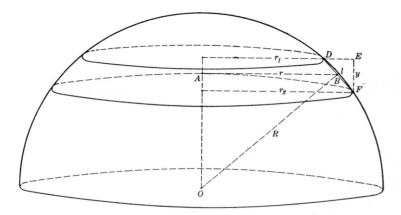

assume arc DF = chord $DF = l$ (the error introduced by taking arc DF = chord DF may be made as small as we please by taking y sufficiently small), the surface of the hemisphere included between these planes is equal to the lateral surface of the inscribed frustum of a right circular cone. This frustum has a slant height l, an altitude y, and base radii r_1 and r_2. Its lateral surface is, by §29,

$$S = \left(\frac{2\pi r_1 + 2\pi r_2}{2}\right) l,$$

or

$$S = 2\pi \left(\frac{r_1 + r_2}{2} \right) l. \tag{1}$$

Let B be the midpoint of chord DF. Then OB is perpendicular to chord DF and within the limits of the approximation is equal to the radius R of the sphere. Denote the radius AB of the mid-section of the frustum by r. Since r is the mid-section of a trapezoid,

$$r = \frac{r_1 + r_2}{2}. \tag{2}$$

We observe that, since angles AOB and FDE have their sides respectively perpendicular, they are equal and right triangles AOB and FDE are similar. Therefore

$$\frac{r}{R} = \frac{y}{l},$$

or

$$r = \frac{Ry}{l}. \tag{3}$$

Substituting in equation (3) the value of r from equation (2), we get

$$\frac{r_1 + r_2}{2} = \frac{Ry}{l}.$$

Substituting this value of $\dfrac{r_1 + r_2}{2}$ in formula (1), we obtain

$$S = 2\pi Ry.$$

By thinking of a sphere as being formed by an indefinitely large number of these frustums, the sum of whose altitudes is $2R$, it is evident that the formula for the surface of a sphere of radius R is

$$S = 2\pi R(2R),$$

or

$$S = 4\pi R^2.$$

Volume analysis. Consider the hemisphere cut from the sphere of center O and radius R. Compare this hemisphere with the solid which results from removing a right circular cone of base radius

R and altitude R from a right circular cylinder of the same base and altitude, as shown in the figure.

Place the two solids so that their bases lie in the same plane. Pass a plane parallel to and distant y from the bases, cutting the

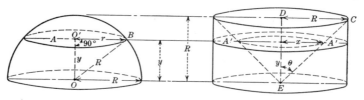

hemisphere in small circle A and the other solid in section A' (area bounded by two concentric circles as shown). Denote the radius of circle A by r, the inner radius of section A' by x (the outer radius of section A' is obviously R), and write

$$A = \pi r^2, \tag{1}$$

$$A' = \pi(R^2 - x^2). \tag{2}$$

Since the legs of right triangle CDE are each R, $\theta = 45°$. Whence $x = y$.

Applying the Pythagorean theorem to right triangle $OO'B$, we have

$$r^2 = R^2 - y^2.$$

Substituting this value of r^2 in equation (1), and putting $x = y$ in equation (2), we obtain

$$A = \pi(R^2 - y^2)$$

and

$$A' = \pi(R^2 - y^2).$$

From these equations we have

$$A = A'.$$

Since the altitude of each solid is equal to R and since $A = A'$, it follows from Cavalieri's theorem that the volumes of the two solids are equal. But, denoting the volume of the constructed solid by V_1, we have

$$V_1 = \text{volume of cylinder} - \text{volume of cone,}$$

or

$$V_1 = (\pi R^2)R - \tfrac{1}{3}(\pi R^2)R = \tfrac{2}{3}\pi R^3.$$

Therefore the volume of the hemisphere is

$$V_1 = \tfrac{2}{3}\pi R^3.$$

Hence the volume of a sphere of radius R is

$$V = \tfrac{4}{3}\pi R^3.$$

Example 1. Find the area of a section cut from a sphere of radius R by a plane distant $R/2$ from the center of the sphere.

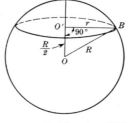

Solution. The given plane cuts from the sphere the small circle of center O' as shown in the figure.

From any point B on the circumference of this small circle draw the radius $BO' = r$, and draw the radius of the sphere $BO = R$. The radius OA which passes through O' is perpendicular to $O'B$. Hence angle $OO'B = 90°$.

Applying the Pythagorean theorem to right triangle $OO'B$, we get

$$r = \sqrt{R^2 - \left(\frac{R}{2}\right)^2} = \frac{R\sqrt{3}}{2}.$$

Hence the area of the smaller circle is

$$A = \pi r^2 = \pi\left(\frac{R\sqrt{3}}{2}\right)^2 = \frac{3\pi R^2}{4}. \quad Ans.$$

Example 2. A sphere of radius R is tangent to the vertical walls and the level floor in the corner of a room. What is the diameter of the largest sphere that can be placed in the space between the corner and the given sphere?

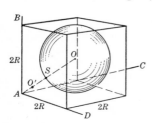

Solution. In the figure, A represents the corner of the room, AB, AC, and AD represent the intersections of the walls and floor, and O represents the center of the given sphere.

Since the given sphere is tangent to each of the two walls and to the floor, its distance from each of these three surfaces is R. Circumscribing a cube of edge $2R$ about the sphere as shown in the figure, we observe that OA is one-half the diagonal of this cube and hence by Prob. 1, §8, $OA = \sqrt{3}R$. This diagonal OA intersects the surface of the given sphere at point S, which is distant R from O.

The center, O', of the required sphere lies on the line OA. The required sphere is tangent to the given sphere at point S. If we let r be the radius of the required sphere, we find by the method used in the case of the given sphere,

$$O'A = \sqrt{3}r. \tag{a}$$

But we also have

$$O'A = SA - SO' = (OA - R) - r = \sqrt{3}R - R - r. \tag{b}$$

Equating the values of $O'A$ from (a) and (b), we get

$$\sqrt{3}r = \sqrt{3}R - R - r.$$

Solving this equation for r, we find

$$r = \frac{\sqrt{3} - 1}{\sqrt{3} + 1} R = (2 - \sqrt{3})R = \mathbf{0.2679R}. \quad Ans.$$

PROBLEMS

1. Show that for a sphere of diameter D, the formula for (a) the area of the surface is

$$S = \pi D^2,$$

(b) the volume is

$$V = \frac{\pi}{6} D^3.$$

2. Find the weight of a snowball 4 ft. in diameter if the wet compact snow of which this ball is made weighs 30 lb. per cu. ft.

3. An iron ball 4 in. in diameter weighs 9 lb. Find the weight of an iron shell 2 in. thick whose external diameter is 20 in.

4. The surface of a hemispherical dome whose diameter is 36 ft. is to be covered with gold leaf which costs 15 cents per square inch. What must be paid for the gold leaf?

5. A cubic foot of ivory weighs 114 lb. Find the weight of 1000 ivory billiard balls $2\frac{1}{2}$ in. in diameter.

6. A spherical balloon is inflated so that its diameter is 40 ft. Find the surface area in the balloon's covering and the volume of the gas.

7. A steel plant has to fill an order from an automobile manufacturer for 100,000 steel ball bearings $\frac{1}{2}$ in. in diameter. What is the total weight of the metal required to fill this order, if steel weighs 480 lb. per cu. ft.?

8. Find the volume and total surface area of the earth. (Consider the earth a perfect sphere of diameter 7960 miles.)

9. An igloo or Eskimo hut is built in the form of a hemispherical shell with an inside diameter of 12 ft. If the igloo is constructed of snow blocks having a uniform thickness of 2 ft. and weighing 40 lb. per cu. ft., find the weight of the igloo, neglecting the entrance. Also, if fresh air contains 0.04 per cent carbon dioxide, find the amount of this gas in the igloo when freshly ventilated.

10. A store sells the same quality of oranges graded as to size. A grade of orange $2\frac{1}{2}$ in. in diameter sells for 35 cents per dozen. What should be the cost of a grade 2 in. in diameter?

11. A layer of equal spheres is in the form of a square. The spheres are arranged so that each sphere is tangent to every one adjacent to it. In the spaces between sets of 4 adjacent spheres, other spheres rest, equal in size to the original. These spheres form in turn a second layer on top of the first. Successive layers of this sort form a pyramidal pile with a single sphere resting on top. If the bottom layer contains 16 spheres, what is the height of the pile in terms of the common radius r of the spheres.

12. Find the volume and total area of a sphere which circumscribes a cylinder of revolution whose altitude and diameter are each 6 in.

13. Find the volume of the largest cube that can be cut from a sphere of diameter 5 in.

14. Compare the volume of a sphere inscribed in a cube with the volume of a sphere that circumscribes the cube.

15. A boy who had discovered that three $\frac{3}{4}$-in. marbles fitted snugly into the bottom of a cylindrical jar, dropped in a fourth on top of the three and poured water enough into the jar to just cover them. How much water did he use?

16. Two balls, one 6 in. in diameter and the other 4 in. in diameter, are placed in a cylindrical jar 9 in. in diameter, as shown. Find the volume of water necessary to cover them.

17. Find the area of the surface and the volume of the sphere circumscribed about a regular tetrahedron of edge 10 in. (see figure).

18. A cone circumscribes a sphere and has its slant height equal to the diameter of its base. Show that the volume of the cone is $\frac{9}{4}$ the volume of the sphere.

19. If in Prob. 18 a plane is passed through the circle of contact, show that the volume of the cone formed is $\frac{9}{32}$ the volume of the sphere.

★20. A sphere of diameter 1.67 in. rests in a conical wine glass whose semi-vertical angle $\theta = 21°$. If the glass contains just enough wine to touch the bottom of the sphere, find the quantity of wine in the glass.

21. Each of the twelve edges of a cube of edge a is tangent to a sphere. Find the volume of that portion of the cube which lies outside the sphere.

34. TERRESTRIAL SPHERE

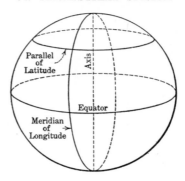

Properties

1. To find the great-circle distances between points on the earth's surface we consider the earth to be a sphere of approximately 3960-mile radius. More exactly, the radius is such that the length of 1 minute of arc of a great circle (1 nautical mile) is 6080 ft.

2. The diameter about which the earth rotates is called the axis of the earth.

3. The extremities of the axis are called the north and south poles.

4. The equator is the circumference of the great circle which is perpendicular to the axis.

5. Meridians are great circles passing through the poles of the earth. Thus all meridians are perpendicular to the equator.

6. The latitude of a point is its angular distance north or south of the equator, measured along a meridian. Parallels of latitude are small circles parallel to the equator.

7. The longitude of a point is the angle at the poles between a fixed meridian and the meridian passing through the point. The fixed meridian is the meridian of Greenwich, England, or of Washington, and is taken as the zero meridian.

8. Longitude is taken positive to the west and negative to the east of the zero meridian from 0° to 180°, or in time units from 0 hour to 12 hours.

35. ZONE

Definition. *A zone is that portion of the surface of a sphere included between two parallel planes.*

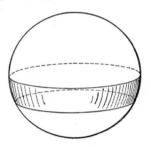

Properties

1. The circumferences of the sections made by the planes are called the *bases* of the zone, and the distance between the planes is the *altitude* of the zone.

2. A zone of *one base* is a zone one of whose bounding planes is tangent to the sphere.

Formulas

The area of any zone is equal to the product of its altitude and the circumference of a great circle of the sphere.

Area = altitude × circumference of great circle.

$$Z = 2\pi Rh.$$

Analysis. The analysis of a zone is essentially the same as the surface analysis of a sphere.   It is left as an exercise for the student to write this analysis.

Example. A spherical ball of radius 3 in. is dropped into a conical vessel of depth 8 in. and radius of base 6 in.   What is the area of the portion of the sphere which lies above the circle of contact with the cone?

Solution. Pass a plane through the axis $O'B$ of the cone, forming the section ABA' as shown on page 96.   This plane intersects the sphere in the great circle $O'CC'$. $OC = 3$ is a radius of this sphere. The sphere is tangent to the cone in the small circle CC' whose center is D.   This circle is the circle of contact between sphere and cone, and is the base of the required zone. The altitude of this zone is $h = 3 + OD$. Since the sides of angles OCD and ABO' are respectively

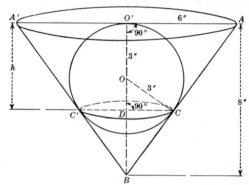

perpendicular, angles OCD and ABO' are equal, and right triangles OCD and ABO' are similar.

Therefore

$$\frac{OD}{3} = \frac{6}{AB}. \qquad (a)$$

Applying the Pythagorean theorem to triangle BAO', we have

$$AB = \sqrt{8^2 + 6^2} = 10.$$

Substituting this value of AB in equation (a), we have

$$\frac{OD}{3} = \frac{6}{10}$$

or

$$OD = 1.8.$$

Substituting $R = 3$ and $h = 3 + OD = 3 + 1.8 = 4.8$ in the formula

$$Z = 2\pi Rh,$$

we get

$$Z = 2\pi (3)(4.8) = 28.8\pi = \mathbf{90.478 \ sq. \ in.} \quad Ans.$$

PROBLEMS

1. Show that the area of a zone of one base (see figure) is equal to the area of the circle whose radius is the chord c of the generating arc AB of the zone.

2. Show that the areas of zones on the same sphere or equal spheres are to each other as their altitudes.

3. The altitude of the torrid zone is 3200 miles. Find its area, assuming the earth to be a sphere with a radius of 3960 miles.

4. A kettle-drum consists of a large bowl of copper with parchment stretched over the opening. If the greatest depth of the drum is 2 ft. and the outer surface of the copper bowl is spherical with a diameter of $2\frac{1}{2}$ ft., find the area of the outer surface of copper.

5. A spherical wooden ball 1 ft. in diameter is used as a float for a boat. If the ball sinks to a depth of 7 in., find the area of the wetted surface.

6. A wooden sphere of radius 15 in. rests in a circular hole in a board. The radius of the hole is 5 in. How far below the upper surface of the board does the sphere extend?

7. A wooden ball 11.15 in. in diameter sinks to a depth of 9.37 in. in water. Find the area of the wetted surface.

8. Find the area illuminated by a candle h feet from the surface of a ball r feet in radius. How much surface is illuminated when a candle is 10 ft. away from a ball 5 ft. in radius?

9. What part of the surface of the earth is included between the parallels 30° N and 60° N?

10. How much of the earth's surface would a man see if he were raised to the height of a diameter above it?

11. An observer at sea is 30 ft. above the surface of the water. How much of the ocean can he see?

12. A candle is 8 ft. 6 in. from the surface of a sphere 12 ft. in diameter. Find the area of the surface illuminated.

13. The center O of a fixed sphere is on the surface of another sphere of center O' as shown in the figure. Show that the area of that portion of the surface of sphere O' which lies within sphere O is equal to the area of a great circle of the sphere O, provided the radius of sphere O is not greater than the diameter of sphere O'.

★**14.** A spherical ball of radius 3.5 in. is dropped into a conical vessel whose vertex angle is 73° 30′. What is the area of the portion of the sphere which lies above the circle of contact with the cone?

36. SPHERICAL SEGMENT

Definition. *A spherical segment is a solid bounded by a zone and the planes of the zone's bases.*

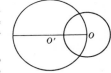

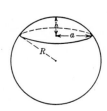

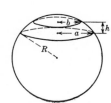

Properties

1. The bases of a spherical segment are the sections made by the parallel planes.

2. If one of the parallel planes is tangent to the sphere, the segment is called a segment of one base.

3. The *altitude* of a spherical segment is the perpendicular distance between the bases.

Formulas

The area of the surface of a spherical segment equals the area of the zone plus the sum of the areas of the bases (or base).

$$Total\ area = (area\ of\ zone) + (areas\ of\ bases).$$
$$T = Z + A_1 + A_2.$$

For a spherical segment of one base, $A_2 = 0$.

The volume of a spherical segment of two bases is given by the following formula.

$$V = \tfrac{1}{6}\pi h(3a^2 + 3b^2 + h^2).$$

For a spherical segment of one base, $b = 0$.

It is interesting to note that we may think of the volume of

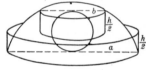

a spherical segment of altitude h and radii a and b as equivalent to the volume (see figure) of a sphere of radius $h/2$ plus the sum of the volumes of two cylinders whose altitudes are each $h/2$ and whose radii are a and b, respectively.

Note. The volume of a spherical segment of one base is also given by the formula

$$V = \frac{\pi h^2}{3}(3R - h).$$

This formula is derived in Ex. 1.

Surface analysis. The surface of a spherical segment of two bases is the sum of the areas of its bases plus the area of the bounding zone. Denoting the areas of the bases by A_1 and A_2 and the area of the zone by Z, we write

$$T = Z + A_1 + A_2.$$

For a spherical segment of one base, evidently $A_2 = 0$.

Volume analysis. Consider the two solids represented by the figures below, which are the same as those on page 90.

Place the two solids so that their bases lie in the same plane. Pass a plane parallel to and distant x from the bases, cutting the hemisphere in a small circle of radius b and the other solid in a section bounded by two concentric circles of radii R and r_1. Pass a second plane parallel to and distant $x + h$ from the bases, cutting the hemisphere in a small circle of radius a and the other solid in a section bounded by two concentric circles of radii R

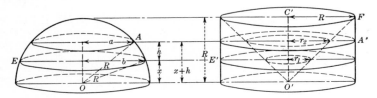

and r_2. These planes cut from the hemisphere the segment of a sphere AE and cut from the other solid the solid $A'E'$, which consists of a right circular cylinder of radius of base R and altitude h minus a frustum of a right circular cone of the same altitude.

From §33, a plane passed parallel to and distant y from the bases of the solids AE and $A'E'$ cuts equal sections from the solids. Since these sections are equal and since the altitude of each solid is h, it follows from Cavalieri's theorem that the volumes of the two solids are equal.

From §33 angle $C'O'F = 45°$. Hence $r_1 = x$ and $r_2 = x + h$. By construction,

Volume $A'E'$ = volume of cylinder − volume of frustum

or

$$V = \pi R^2 h - \frac{h\pi}{3} [x^2 + (x + h)^2 + x(x + h)]$$

or

$$V = \pi R^2 h - \frac{h\pi}{3} (3x^2 + 3xh + h^2). \tag{1}$$

But from the figure of the segment, we write

$$x^2 = R^2 - b^2 \tag{2}$$

and

$$(x + h)^2 = R^2 - a^2. \tag{3}$$

Expanding the left-hand member of equation (3) and subtracting (2) from (3), member by member, we get

$$2xh + h^2 = b^2 - a^2.$$

Multiplying this equation by 3 and solving for $3hx$, we obtain

$$3hx = \tfrac{3}{2}(b^2 - a^2 - h^2). \tag{4}$$

Substituting in (1) the value of x^2 from (2) and the value of $3hx$ from (4), we get

$$V = \pi R^2 h - \frac{h\pi}{3}[3(R^2 - b^2) + \tfrac{3}{2}(b^2 - a^2 - h^2) + h^2],$$

or, after slight simplification,

$$V = \frac{\pi h}{6}(3a^2 + 3b^2 + h^2).$$

Example 1.   Show that the volume of a spherical segment of one base is given by the formula

$$V = \tfrac{1}{3}\pi h^2(3R - h).$$

Solution.   Right triangle OAB shown in the figure lies in the plane of a great circle of the sphere whose center is O. $OB = R$ is the radius of the sphere, $AB = a$ is the radius of the base of the segment, and h is the altitude of the segment.

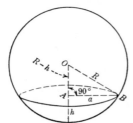

Applying the Pythagorean theorem to triangle OAB, we have

$$a^2 = R^2 - (R - h)^2$$

or

$$a^2 = 2Rh - h^2.$$

Substituting this value of a^2 and $b = 0$ in the formula

$$V = \tfrac{1}{6}\pi h(3a^2 + 3b^2 + h^2),$$

we get

$$V = \tfrac{1}{6}\pi h[3(2Rh - h^2) + h^2],$$

or

$$V = \tfrac{1}{3}\pi h^2(3R - h). \quad Ans.$$

Example 2.   A spherical bowl was filled to a depth of 6 in. with a mixture compounded from equal parts of two liquids, one white and the other red.   After standing for a short time the mixture separated, the red liquid settling below the white.   If the thickness of the segment of white liquid is 2 in., find the volume of liquid in the bowl.

Solution.   Referring to the figure, we note that the space occupied by the total amount of liquid in the bowl is a spherical segment of one base whose altitude is 6 in., and that the space occupied by the red liquid is also a spherical segment of one base whose altitude is $h = 6 - 2 = 4$ in.

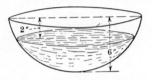

Denote by V the volume of the entire contents of the bowl, and by V_1 the volume of red liquid.   Using the formula derived in Ex. 1, we write

$$V = \frac{\pi 6^2}{3}(3R - 6), \qquad (a)$$

and

$$V_1 = \frac{\pi 4^2}{3}(3R - 4).$$

Since we are given that $V = 2V_1$, we have

$$\left(\frac{\pi 6^2}{3}\right)(3R - 6) = 2\left(\frac{\pi 4^2}{3}\right)(3R - 4).$$

Solving this equation for R, we get

$$R = \frac{22}{3}.$$

Substituting this value of R in equation (a), we find the volume of liquid to be

$$V = \frac{\pi 6^2}{3}\left[3\left(\frac{22}{3}\right) - 6\right] = 192\pi = \textbf{603.19 cu. in.}\quad \textit{Ans.}$$

PROBLEMS

1. Show that the volume of a spherical segment of one base of altitude h and radius a is equivalent to the volume (see figure) of a sphere of radius $h/2$, plus the volume of a cylinder of altitude $h/2$ and radius a.

2. Show that for a spherical segment of one base the total area is $T = \pi h(4R - h)$, where h is the altitude of the segment and R is the radius of the sphere.

3. The inside of a wash basin is in the shape of a segment of a sphere; the distance across the top is 18 in. and its greatest depth is 7 in. Find how many pints of water it will hold, reckoning 7.48 gal. to the cubic foot.

4. A hollow glass bowl in the shape of a sphere of radius 4 in. is filled with water to a depth of 3 in. Find the volume of the water. If the water flows out through a small hole in the bottom so that the level drops 2 in., how much water has escaped?

5. The water in a hemispherical bowl 18 in. across the top is 6 in. deep. What percentage of the capacity of the bowl is filled?

6. A 6-in. spherical float is used as a location mark for a rowboat anchor. It floats in salt water. Find the depth to which the float sinks if the material of which the float is made weighs $16\frac{1}{3}$ lb. per cu. ft. and salt water weighs 63 lb. per cu. ft.

7. An experimental laboratory fills 100 globes with a certain gas to intensify the lighting effect. The space occupied by the gas in each globe is a spherical segment of one base the radius of whose sphere is 6 in. If the altitude of the segment is 5 in., find the volume of gas required.

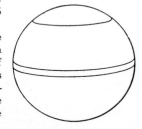

8. Suppose an orange to be a perfect sphere whose diameter is 3 in., and suppose that the skin is of uniform thickness $\frac{1}{8}$ in. and that the juice of the orange is uniformly distributed throughout its meat. Find the depth of a slice cut from the outside that will contain as much juice as a slice whose bases are parallel sections $\frac{1}{8}$ in. from the center.

9. The center of each of two spheres of radius R lies in the surface of the other sphere. Find the volume common to the two spheres.

10. A gallon of water is poured into a spherical bowl of radius 5.72 in. Denote the depth of the water at the deepest point by h, and write an equation from which the value of h may be obtained. Show that $h = 4.11$ in. satisfies this equation approximately.

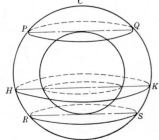

11. The figure represents two concentric spheres of radii a and $a - d$. PQ and RS are parallel tangent planes. HK is a plane parallel to PQ and RS, cutting the spheres at any position between PQ and RS. Prove that the area intercepted on HK *between the spheres* is constant. Hence show that the space between the spheres included between planes PQ and RS is

$$2\pi(a - d)(2a - d)d.$$

Hence prove that the volume of the spherical segment PCQ is

$$\tfrac{1}{3}\pi d^2(3a - d).$$

★**12.** Find the diameter of the surface of the water in Prob. 10.

37. SPHERICAL SECTOR

Definition. *A spherical sector is a solid generated by rotating a sector of a circle about an axis which passes through the center of the circle but which contains no point inside the sector.*

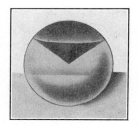

Properties

1. The bounding surfaces of a spherical sector are a zone, which is called the *base*, and one or two conical surfaces.

2. A spherical sector having only one conical surface is called a *spherical cone*.

Formulas

The surface area of a spherical sector is equal to the area of the zone which forms its base plus the sum of the lateral areas of the bounding cones (or cone).

Total area = zone + lateral area of bounding cones.

$$T = Z + S_1 + S_2.$$

For a spherical cone, $S_2 = 0$.

The volume of a spherical sector is equal to one-third of the product of the area of the zone which forms its base, and the radius of the sphere.

Volume = $\frac{1}{3}$ zone × radius of sphere.

$$V = \tfrac{1}{3}ZR.$$

Surface analysis. In a spherical sector having two conical surfaces let T be the total area of the sector, let S_1 and S_2 be the areas of the conical surfaces, and let Z be the area of the zone which forms the base of the sector. The area of the surface of the sector is the sum of the areas of the conical surfaces plus the area of the zone, or in symbols

$$T = Z + S_1 + S_2.$$

For a spherical cone, $S_2 = 0$.

Volume analysis. In the figure is shown a spherical cone. The radius and altitude of its zone are denoted by b and h, respectively, and the radius of its sphere by R. Denoting the volume of the sector by V, the volume of the cone by V_c, and the volume of the segment by V_s, we write

$$V = V_c + V_s, \tag{1}$$

an equation which is illustrated by the following figure:

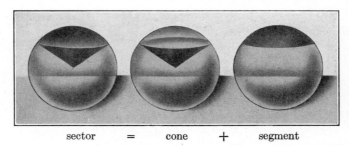

sector   =   cone   +   segment

The volume of the cone is

$$V_c = \tfrac{1}{3}(\pi b^2)(R - h). \tag{2}$$

The volume of the segment (see Ex. 1, §36) is

$$V_s = \tfrac{1}{3}\pi h^2(3R - h). \tag{3}$$

Substituting in (1) the values of V_c from (2) and V_s from (3), we obtain

$$V = \tfrac{1}{3}\pi b^2(R - h) + \tfrac{1}{3}\pi h^2(3R - h). \tag{4}$$

Applying the Pythagorean theorem to right triangle OAB (see figure), we have

$$b^2 = R^2 - (R - h)^2 = 2Rh - h^2.$$

Substituting this value of b^2 in (4) and simplifying, we find

$$V = \tfrac{1}{3}(2\pi Rh)R.$$

But the area of the zone of the sector is

$$Z = 2\pi Rh.$$

Hence

$$V = \tfrac{1}{3}ZR.$$

The volume V of a sector having two conical surfaces and of base Z is the difference between two spherical cones of bases say Z_1 and Z_2, respectively. Therefore we write

$$V = \tfrac{1}{3}Z_1R - \tfrac{1}{3}Z_2R,$$

an equation illustrated by the following figures:

 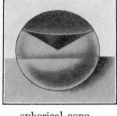 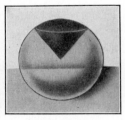

| sector | = | spherical cone | − | spherical cone |

Factoring, we write

$$V = \tfrac{1}{3}R(Z_1 - Z_2).$$

But since $Z_1 - Z_2 = Z$, we have

$$V = \tfrac{1}{3}ZR.$$

Example. Find the volume of a spherical cone if the chord of the generating arc of its zone is $\sqrt{20}$ in. and the radius of its zone is 4 in.

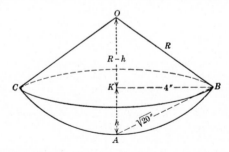

Solution. Pass a plane through the axis of the sector $OA = R$ (see figure), forming the axial section $OBAC$. Drop perpendicular BK

to OA.　$BK = 4$ in. is the radius of the zone.　To find its altitude h we apply the Pythagorean theorem to the right triangle AKB and obtain

$$h = \sqrt{(\sqrt{20})^2 - 4^2} = 2. \qquad (a)$$

Applying the Pythagorean theorem to right triangle OKB, we have

$$R^2 - (R - h)^2 = 4^2.$$

Substituting in this equation $h = 2$ from (a) and solving for R, we obtain

$$R = 5.$$

Substituting $R = 5$ and $Z = 2\pi Rh = 2\pi(5)\,(2) = 20\pi$ in the formula

$$V = \tfrac{1}{3}ZR,$$

we find

$$V = \tfrac{1}{3}(20\pi)\,(5) = \frac{100\pi}{3} = \textbf{104.72 cu. in.}\quad Ans.$$

PROBLEMS

1. A top is cast in the form of a spherical sector.　The slant height of the conical portion is 2 in. and the element of the cone is inclined 30° to the axis. Find the cost of material in manufacturing 1000 such tops if the material used costs 90 cents a cubic foot.

2. An imitation pearl eardrop consists of a spherical segment which is surmounted by a cone.　The cone and the segment have a common base.　The slant height of the cone is equal to the radius of the sphere of which the segment is a part.　Find the amount of material used in manufacturing 100,000 of these eardrops if the radius of the sphere is $\frac{1}{2}$ in. and the altitude of the surmounting cone is $\frac{3}{8}$ in.

3. The lower portion of a perfume dropper is made of solid glass and is in the shape of a spherical cone.　The altitude of the conical part is 2 in., and the radius of the base is $\frac{1}{4}$ in.; find the volume of glass used to make the glass portion of 20,000 droppers.

4. A knob on a colonial bedpost is in the shape of a spherical cone whose base measures $1\frac{1}{2}$ sq. in., and the radius of the sphere from which it is cut is 3 in.　Find the volume of wood contained in the ornament.

5. A marline spike, a nautical tool used for opening or separating the strands of a rope in splicing, is in the shape of a spherical cone the radius of whose sphere is $1\frac{1}{2}$ ft. and the area of whose zone is 1 sq. in.　Find the weight of 100 spikes if they are made of iron which weighs 450 lb. per cu. ft.

★**6.** Solve Prob. 1 if the element of the cone is inclined 33° 45′ to the axis.

38. MISCELLANEOUS PROBLEMS

1. Find the volume of the earth's atmosphere if it extends 50 miles in height and the earth is considered a sphere of 3960-mile radius.

2. What will it cost to gild the surface of a globe whose radius is $1\frac{1}{2}$ decimeters, at an average cost of $\frac{2}{3}$ cent per square centimeter?

3. The outside diameter of a spherical copper shell 2 in. thick is 14 in. Find its weight if a cubic inch of copper weighs 5.1 oz.

4. In order to double the capacity of a spherical balloon, by what percentage must the area of the material in its surface be increased?

5. A top consists of a spherical segment and a cone. If the altitude of the segment is 1 in., the radius of the common base 3 in., and the altitude of the cone 6 in., find: (*a*) the total surface of the top; (*b*) the volume of the top.

6. A terrestrial globe is 20 in. in diameter. A plane is passed so as to cut from the globe a circular section 16 in. in diameter. Find the area of the smaller zone determined by this section.

7. What is the distance of the horizon on a calm sea from a point 25 ft. in height, assuming that the line of vision is in a straight line?

8. To what height must a man be raised above the earth in order to see one-fourth of its surface?

9. A 4-in. auger hole is bored through a 10-in. sphere, the axis of the hole coinciding with a diameter of the sphere. Find the volume bored out.

10. The ball of a float valve has a diameter of 4 in., and the thickness of the metal is 0.05 in. How much does it weigh if it is made of copper? (Copper weighs 556 lb. per cu. ft.)

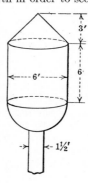

11. A factory's pressure tank rests on the upper base of a vertical pipe whose inside diameter is $1\frac{1}{2}$ ft. and whose length is 40 ft. The tank is a vertical cylinder surmounted by a cone, and it has a hemispherical base. If the altitudes of the cylinder and the cone are respectively 6 ft. and 3 ft. and if all three parts of the tank have an inside diameter of 6 ft., find the volume of water in the tank and pipe when full.

12. Four grapefruit (considered spheres) 6 in. in diameter are placed in a square box whose inside base dimensions are 12 in. In the space between the first four grapefruit a fifth of the same diameter is placed. How deep must the box be so that the top will just touch the fifth grapefruit?

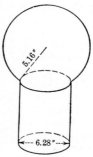

13. A cylindrical post 6.28 in. in diameter is surmounted by a part of a sphere 5.16 in. in radius, as shown in the figure. Find the surface and the volume of the part of the sphere used.

14. Given a right circular cone of altitude R and radius of base R, a hemisphere of radius R, and a right circular cylinder of altitude R and radius R, prove that their volumes are in arithmetical progression.

15. A hollow sphere of radius R is surmounted by a hollow right circular cone. The elements of the cone are tangent to the sphere, and the base of the cone is a small circle of the sphere. The vertex of the cone is distant R from the surface of the sphere. (a) Find the volume common to the sphere and the cone. (b) Find the volume of the cone.

16. One edge of a cube coincides with a radius of a sphere. If the radius of the sphere is R, find the volume of that portion of the cube which lies outside the sphere.

17. Find the volume of the largest right circular cylinder of altitude 8 in. that can be cut from a sphere of diameter 12 in.

18. A slide in a machine is to run on rolling balls. The balls run in grooves with straight sides as shown. The angle of the upper (moving) groove is 120°, and that of the lower (fixed) groove is 90°. What size balls should be used?

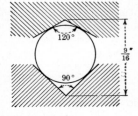

19. A cone is inscribed in a sphere. It has for its base a great circle of the sphere and for its vertex a pole of that circle. Find the ratio (a) of the total area of the cone to the area of the sphere, (b) of the volume of the cone to the volume of the sphere.

20. A sphere of radius 6.87 in. rests in a circular hole of radius 5.13 in. How far below the plane of the hole does the sphere extend?

21. The diameter of a sphere coincides with the axis of a right circular cone, and the surface of the cone intersects the surface of the sphere in a great circle. Find: (a) the vertical angle of the cone; (b) the volume of the cone; (c) the volume common to the two solids; (d) the volume of that portion of the cone which lies outside the sphere; (e) the volume of that portion of the sphere which lies outside the cone. Denote radius of sphere by R.

22. Solve Prob. 21 if (a) $R = 2$; (b) $R = 3.72$.

23. The center of each of three spheres of radius R lies in the surfaces of the other two. Pass a plane containing the centers of the spheres. Find the area common to the three great circles cut from the spheres by this plane.

24. A sphere is inscribed in a right circular cone of altitude h and radius of base r. Write a formula in terms of r and h for the volume of the sphere.

25. A right circular cylinder with altitude equal to the diameter of its base is inscribed in a sphere. (a) Compare the lateral area of the cylinder with the area of the sphere. (b) Compare the volume of the sphere with that of the cylinder.

26. The diameter of a sphere is 18 in. Find the volume of the largest regular pyramid of altitude 15 in. that can be cut from the sphere if the pyramid is (a) square, (b) pentagonal, (c) hexagonal, (d) octagonal.

27. The diameter of the base of a right circular cone is 10 in., and its altitude is 8 in. Find the volume of the largest sphere that can be cut from the cone.

28. A right circular cone is inscribed in a sphere whose diameter is $\frac{4}{3}$ the altitude of the cone. Show that the lateral surface and the volume of the cone are, respectively, $\frac{2}{3}$ and $\frac{9}{32}$ of the surface and volume of the sphere.

29. Compare the volume of a sphere with the volume of the circumscribed regular tetrahedron (see figure).

30. Four balls of radius 2 are placed in a square box whose inside base edge is 10. In the space between these balls a fifth ball is placed. Find the minimum depth of the box in order that the cover will just touch the fifth ball, if its radius is (*a*) 3; (*b*) 4.

31. A spherical ball of radius R is dropped into a vessel in the form of an inverted right circular cone. Find the radius and altitude of the cone, if when three more balls each of radius R are dropped into it they form a layer on top of the first ball such that all four balls are tangent to each other and in addition each ball of the upper layer is tangent both to the side and to the top of the vessel.

32. A diameter of a sphere of radius R coincides with an element of a right circular cylinder of diameter R. For the solid common to the sphere and the cylinder, find the area of a section made by (*a*) a plane containing the axis of the cylinder and the diameter of the sphere which coincides with the element of the cylinder, (*b*) the plane perpendicular to the axis of the cylinder at its midpoint, ★(*c*) a plane containing the axis of the cylinder and perpendicular to the plane of (*a*).

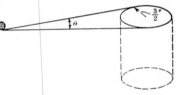

★**33.** The center of a golfball (see figure) is 6 ft. from the center of the top of the cylindrical cup of radius $\frac{3}{2}$ in. Within what angle θ must the ball be struck if it is to drop into the hole?

★**34.** A cylinder of radius a passes centrally through a sphere of radius r. Show that the volume removed from the sphere is the difference of two spheres one of radius r and the other of radius $r\cos\theta$, where $\sin\theta = a/r$.

★**35.** A right circular cone with vertical angle α has its vertex at the center of a sphere of radius r. Show that the volume common to the cone and sphere is $\frac{2}{3}\pi r^3(1 - \cos\frac{1}{2}\alpha)$.

CHAPTER VII

VOLUMES AND SURFACES OF REVOLUTION
POLYHEDRONS

39. CENTER OF GRAVITY

For any body there is a point at which the body may be supported in any position with no tendency to turn.   This point is called the *center of gravity* of the body.

By considering the point where a body must be held so that the body will hang balanced (see figures), one can see by inspection that the center of gravity (c.g.) of:

(*a*) a straight *line segment* is at its midpoint (see figure);

(*b*) a *rectangle* is at the intersection of its diagonals (see figure);

(*c*) a *triangle* is at the intersection of its medians (see figure);

(*d*) a *circle* is at its center (see figure).

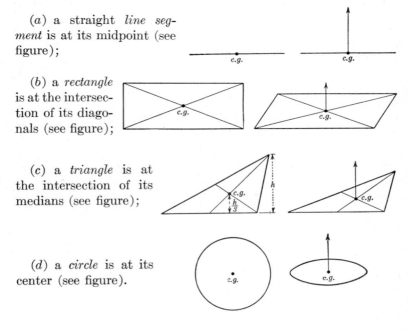

40. THEOREMS OF PAPPUS

First Theorem.   *The area of any surface generated by the revolution of a plane curve about an external axis in its plane is equal*

to the product of the length of the generating curve and the distance
its center of gravity moves.

An axis in the same plane with a curve is external to the curve
if every point of the curve lies on a given side of the axis or on
the axis.

Surface = distance c.g. moves × length of curve.

$$S = \left(\frac{\alpha}{360°} 2\pi \bar{x}\right) L,$$

where α is the angle in degrees generated by the revolution of the
line drawn from the axis of revolution to the center of gravity,
and $\bar{x}$ is the distance of the center of gravity from the axis.

Second Theorem. *The volume of any solid generated by the
revolution of a plane area about an external axis in its plane is equal
to the product of the area of the generating figure and the distance its
center of gravity moves.*

An axis in the same plane with a plane area is external to the
area if no two points of the area are on opposite sides of the axis.

Volume = distance c.g. moves × area.

$$V = \left(\frac{\alpha}{360°} 2\pi \bar{x}\right) A,$$

where α is the angle in degrees generated by the revolution of the
line drawn from the axis of revolution to the center of gravity and
$\bar{x}$ is the distance of the center of gravity from the axis.

Historical Note. This theorem was first discovered by Pappus of Alexandria
in the third century of the Christian era, but his work was forgotten until the
sixteenth century, when Kepler and Guldin revived interest in the subject.

Kepler succeeded in finding rules for computing volumes of a number of
solids generated by the revolution of a plane figure. All his rules were special
cases of Pappus's theorem. However, Kepler never announced the theorem in
its general form.

Among the solids treated by Kepler were the torus and two solids which he
termed " the apple " and " the lemon." (" The apple " is the solid which is
formed by revolving a segment of a circle, greater than a semicircle, about its
chord as an axis. " The lemon " is the solid which is formed by revolving a
segment of a circle, less than a semicircle, about its chord as an axis.)

Example 1. Find the area of the surface of revolution generated
by revolving the line MN (see figure, page 112) about the axis AB
parallel to MN.

Solution.   The length of the line MN (generating curve) is $L = l$. For one complete revolution $\alpha = 360°$.

Since MN contains its center of gravity and is distant a from AB, $\bar{x} = a$.

Substituting $\bar{x} = a$, $\alpha = 360°$, and $L = l$ in the formula

$$S = \left(\frac{\alpha}{360°}\, 2\pi\bar{x}\right)L,$$

we find

$$S = 2\pi al.\quad Ans.$$

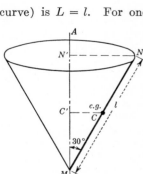

The student should observe that the surface generated in this case is the lateral surface of a right circular cylinder of altitude l and radius of base a.

Example 2.   Find the area of the surface generated by revolving about the axis AB the line MN shown in the figure.

Solution.   The center of gravity of MN is at its midpoint C. Hence $CM = \frac{1}{2}l$. From C drop perpendicular CC' to AB. Then since the shorter leg of a 30°–60° right triangle is equal to half the hypotenuse, we have

$$\bar{x} = CC' = \tfrac{1}{2}CM = \tfrac{1}{4}l.$$

The length of the line MN (generating curve) is $L = l$. For one complete revolution, $\alpha = 360°$. Substituting $\bar{x} = l/4$, $\alpha = 360°$, and $L = l$ in the formula

$$S = \left(\frac{\alpha}{360°}\, 2\pi\bar{x}\right)L,$$

we find

$$S = \frac{\pi l^2}{2}.\quad Ans.$$

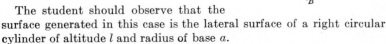

The student should observe that the surface generated in this case is the lateral surface of a right circular cone whose semi-vertical angle is 30° and whose slant height is l.

Example 3. Find the volume generated by revolving about the line AB the rectangle shown in the figure.

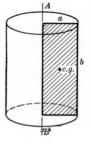

Solution. Since the center of gravity of the rectangle coincides with the center of the rectangle, it is distant $\frac{1}{2}a$ from the axis AB. Hence $\bar{x} = \frac{1}{2}a$. The area of the rectangle (generating figure) is $A = ab$. For a complete revolution, $\alpha = 360°$.

Substituting $\bar{x} = \frac{1}{2}a$, $\alpha = 360°$, and $A = ab$ in the formula

$$V = \left(\frac{\alpha}{360°} 2\pi\bar{x}\right) A,$$

we find

$$V = (2\pi)\ (\tfrac{1}{2}a)\ (ab) = \boldsymbol{\pi a^2 b}. \quad Ans.$$

The student should observe that the solid generated in this case is a right circular cylinder of altitude b and radius of base a.

Example 4. Find the distance of the center of gravity of a semi-circular area of radius r from its diameter.

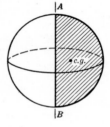

Solution. When the semicircle is revolved about its diameter through an angle $\alpha = 360°$, a sphere of radius r is generated (see figure). The area of the semicircle (generating figure) is $A = \frac{1}{2}\pi r^2$; the volume of the sphere (generated solid) is $V = \frac{4}{3}\pi r^3$.

Substituting $V = \frac{4}{3}\pi r^3$, $\alpha = 360°$, and $A = \frac{1}{2}\pi r^2$ in the formula

$$V = \left(\frac{\alpha}{360°} 2\pi\bar{x}\right) A,$$

we obtain

$$\tfrac{4}{3}\pi r^3 = (2\pi)\ (\bar{x})\ (\tfrac{1}{2}\pi r^2).$$

Solving this equation for $\bar{x}$, we find

$$\bar{x} = \frac{4r}{3\pi}. \quad Ans.$$

Example 5. Find the distance of the center of gravity of a semi-circular arc of radius r from its diameter.

Solution. When the semicircular arc is revolved about its diameter through an angle $\alpha = 360°$, the surface of a sphere of radius r is generated (see figure).   The length of the semicircular arc (generating curve) is $L = \pi r$; the area of the spherical surface (generated surface) is $S = 4\pi r^2$.

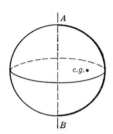

Substituting $S = 4\pi r^2$, $\alpha = 360°$, and $L = \pi r$ in the formula

$$S = \left(\frac{\alpha}{360°} 2\pi \bar{x}\right) L,$$

we obtain

$$4\pi r^2 = (2\pi)\,(\bar{x})\,(\pi r).$$

Solving this equation for $\bar{x}$, we find

$$\bar{x} = \frac{2r}{\pi} \cdot \quad Ans.$$

PROBLEMS

In the following problems cross section means axial section.   An axial section is a section made by a plane containing the axis.

1. Wedding rings a few years ago were merely plain bands of gold with an approximate cross section of $\frac{3}{128}$ sq. in.   In a certain size ring the center of the cross section is $\frac{5}{16}$ in. from the axis of the ring.   Find the amount of gold used in 50,000 such rings.

2. A centrifugal water turbine has a protective circular covering in the shape of the surface of a torus 2 ft. in diameter encasing its entire outer rim. If the center of the cross section is 10 ft. from the center of the wheel, find the volume enclosed by the casing, neglecting the portion cut away for fitting purposes.

3. An inflated tire tube has a cross section, uniformly circular, of 4 in. inside diameter.   The distance of the center of the tube's cross section from the axis of the wheel for which it was made to fit is 14 in.   Find the amount of air in the tube, and also, if the rubber is $\frac{1}{8}$ in. thick, find the outer surface area of the rubber.

4. The cross section of the rim of an iron flywheel 3 ft. in diameter is a rectangle 12 in. by 2 in.   How much does the rim weigh?   (The iron weighs 450 lb. per cu. ft.)

5. An anchor ring is formed by revolving a circle 3 in. in diameter about a line lying in the plane of the circle and at a distance of 10 in. from the center. Find the volume of the solid formed.

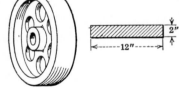

6. A vertical 3-in. steam pipe is turned so as to eventually run horizontally.   The path of the center of the pipe follows along the arc of a circle whose radius is 8 ft.   If the steam pipe is $\frac{1}{4}$ in. thick and if it is covered with a coating of asbestos 2 in. thick, find the amount of asbestos coating in the turn.   (A 3-in. pipe is a pipe which has an inside diameter of 3 in.)

7. In passing an obstruction the center of a steel aqueduct follows along an arc of a circle whose radius is ¼ mile, and the direction of the center is changed by 20°. The aqueduct has a uniform cross section whose inside diameter is 4 ft. Find the volume of water in the turn if the aqueduct is running full.

8. Find the position of the center of gravity of the area of the quadrant of a circle of radius r.

9. Find the position of the center of gravity of the arc of the quadrant of a circle of radius r.

10. For the triangle shown, find the distance of the center of gravity above the 4-ft. base.

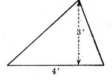

11. Find the position of the center of gravity of the sector of a circle of radius r if the central angle of the sector is 30°.

12. Find the position of the center of gravity of the trapezoid shown in the figure.

13. Prove by means of the First Theorem of Pappus that the area of a circle is $\dfrac{\pi d^2}{4}$, where d is the diameter.

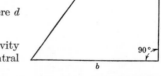

14. Find the position of the center of gravity of an arc of a circle of radius r if the central angle subtended by the arc is 60°.

15. A square and an equilateral triangle having their bases in the same straight line are circumscribed about a circle of radius a. The whole figure is then revolved about an altitude of the triangle. Find, in terms of a: (a) the sum of the areas of the three surfaces generated, (b) the sum of the volumes of the three solids generated.

16. An equilateral triangle is circumscribed about a circle of radius r and the figure is revolved about an altitude of the triangle as an axis. Show that (a) the surface generated by the revolution of the arc of the circle is two-thirds the lateral surface generated by the revolution of the triangle, (b) the volume generated by the revolution of the semicircular area is four-ninths the volume generated by the revolution of the triangle.

17. A segment of a circle of radius R is bounded by an arc equal to ⅓ the circumference of the circle. Find the volume of the solid generated by revolving this segment about its chord as an axis. (This solid is known as Kepler's lemon.)

41. POLYHEDRONS

Definition. *A polyhedron is a solid bounded by polygons.*

Properties

The *edges* of a polyhedron are the intersections of the bounding planes.

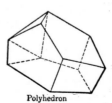

Polyhedron

The *faces* are the portions of the bounding planes included by the edges.

The *vertices* are the intersections of the edges.

A *diagonal* of a polyhedron is a straight line joining two vertices not in the same face.

Definition. A convex polyhedron is a polyhedron every section of which is a convex polygon.

Regular Polyhedrons

Definition. A regular polyhedron is a polyhedron all of whose faces are equal regular polygons, and all of whose polyhedral angles are equal.

There are only five regular polyhedrons, namely:

| Regular Tetrahedron | Cube | Regular Octahedron | Regular Dodecahedron | Regular Icosahedron |

Certain properties of regular polyhedrons are given in the table on page 117. In this table we denote the number of faces by F, number of edges by E, number of vertices by v, area of face by B, radius of inscribed sphere by r, and the length of an edge by e.

Formulas

Total area = number of faces $\times$ area of one face.

$$T = FB.$$

Volume = $\frac{1}{3}$ number of faces $\times$ face $\times$ radius of inscribed sphere.

$$V = \tfrac{1}{3}FBr.$$

Historical Note. Pythagoras knew about the existence of all the regular polyhedrons except the dodecahedron. This was discovered in 470 B.C. by Hippasus, who having boasted of his discovery was drowned by the other Pythagoreans. The regular polyhedrons were supposed to have certain magical properties, and their study was greatly emphasized.

Polyhedron	F	E	v	B	r	Volume
Tetrahedron	4	6	4	$\dfrac{e^2}{4}\sqrt{3}$	$\tfrac{1}{12}e\sqrt{6}$	$\tfrac{1}{12}e^3\sqrt{2}$
Hexahedron (cube)	6	12	8	e^2	$\dfrac{e}{2}$	e^3
Octahedron	8	12	6	$\tfrac{1}{4}e^2\sqrt{3}$	$\tfrac{1}{6}e\sqrt{6}$	$\tfrac{1}{3}e^3\sqrt{2}$
Dodecahedron	12	30	20	$\tfrac{5}{4}e^2\sqrt{\dfrac{3+\sqrt{5}}{5-\sqrt{5}}}$	$e\sqrt{\dfrac{25+11\sqrt{5}}{40}}$	$\dfrac{e^3}{4}(15+7\sqrt{5})$
Icosahedron	20	30	12	$\tfrac{1}{4}e^2\sqrt{3}$	$e\sqrt{\dfrac{7+3\sqrt{5}}{24}}$	$\tfrac{5}{12}e^3(3+\sqrt{5})$

Surface analysis. Since a regular polyhedron has F faces, the total area is equal to F times the area of one face.

Volume analysis. Consider any regular polyhedron of F faces in which is inscribed a sphere of center O and radius r. Divide this polyhedron into pyramids by planes each of which passes through an edge of the polyhedron and all of which contain the center O. Each of these pyramids has as altitude the radius r of the inscribed sphere and as base B a face of the polyhedron. Hence the volume of one pyramid is $\tfrac{1}{3}Br$. Since there are F pyramids, we write for the volume of the polyhedron

$$V = \tfrac{1}{3}FBr.$$

Example. Each corner of a hexahedron (cube) of edge $3a$ is cut off by a plane intersecting three concurrent edges at points each distant a from the vertex of the corner. Find the volume of the solid formed.

Solution. Each of the eight corners cut from the cube is a triangular pyramid such as O–ABC shown in the figure. Consider ABC as the base and O as the vertex of this pyramid. Since ABC is an isosceles right triangle of leg a, the

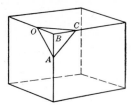

$$\text{Area of } ABC = \frac{(a)\ (a)}{2} = \frac{a^2}{2}.$$

The altitude h of the pyramid is $OB = a$.

Substituting $B = \dfrac{a^2}{2}$ and $h = a$ in the formula

$$V = \tfrac{1}{3}Bh,$$

we get

$$V = \frac{1}{3}\left(\frac{a^2}{2}\right)(a) = \frac{a^3}{6}.$$

Therefore the volume of the eight corners cut from the cube is

$$V_2 = 8\left(\frac{a^3}{6}\right) = \frac{4}{3}a^3.$$

But the volume of the given cube is

$$V_3 = (3a)^3 = 27a^3.$$

Hence for the required volume, we have

$$V_3 - V_2 = 27a^3 - \frac{4}{3}a^3 = \frac{77a^3}{3}. \quad Ans.$$

PROBLEMS

1. For each of the regular polyhedrons verify the formula $E = v + F - 2$ by substituting for E, V, and F the values given in the table on p. 117. This formula is true for all convex polyhedrons.

2. Verify each of the values given in column B of the table on p. 117.

3. Substitute in the formula $V = \tfrac{1}{3}FBr$ the values of F, B, and r given in the table on p. 117 to verify the entries in the column headed Volume.

4. Find the radius of the sphere inscribed in a regular icosahedron whose volume is 24 cu. in.

5. If a regular tetrahedron and a regular octahedron have the same edge, show that the volume of the octahedron is four times the volume of the tetrahedron.

6. If a regular dodecahedron and a regular icosahedron have the same edge, compare (*a*) their surface areas, (*b*) their volumes.

7. How many glass paper weights each in the shape of a dodecahedron 1 in. on an edge can be manufactured by melting 1000 glass paper weights each in the form of a cube 2 in. on an edge?

8. Verify the value of r in the table on p. 117 for (*a*) a regular tetrahedron and (*b*) a regular octahedron without taking the values listed in the columns headed B and Volume.

9. Using the following directions, construct solids representing the five regular polyledrons:

Directions for construction. Mark on cardboard larger figures similar to the drawings. Cut along the full lines. Fold along the dotted lines so as to form the figures. Paste strips of paper along the edges.

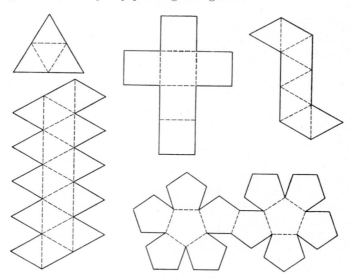

10. A certain polyhedron whose shortest edge is 2 in. weighs 40 lb. What is the weight of a similar polyhedron whose shortest edge is 5 in.?

★**11.** Find the number of degrees in a dihedral angle of a regular tetrahedron.

12. How many diagonals can be drawn in a regular octahedron?

13. The figure represents an octahedron with diagonals $AC = 16$ in., $EF = 12$ in., $BD = 8$ in. Find the total surface and volume. The diagonals are mutually perpendicular, and the point of intersection is the midpoint of each diagonal.

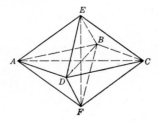

CHAPTER VIII

THE GENERAL PRISMATOID

42. SECTION OF A GENERAL PRISMATOID

Definition. A *general prismatoid* is a solid such that the area of any section, say A_y, parallel to and distant y from a fixed plane can be expressed as a polynomial in y of degree not higher than the third. That is, a solid is a general prismatoid if

$$A_y = ay^3 + by^2 + cy + d,$$

where a, b, c, and d are constants which may be positive, negative, or zero.

Inasmuch as all the solids of Solid Mensuration, and many others considered in advanced mathematics, are such that A_y is expressible as a polynomial in y of degree not higher than the second, we shall confine our discussion to prismatoids for which

$$A_y = ay^2 + by + c.$$

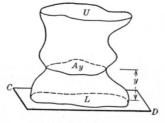

For example, consider a prismatoid with its lower base L lying in the fixed plane CD (see figure). Then the area of a section A_y parallel to the base L and distant y above it will be

$$A_y = ay^2 + by + L.$$

Example 1. For the hemisphere shown in the figure, find the value of A_y where y is the distance from the base of the hemisphere. Also find the area of the mid-section parallel to the base.

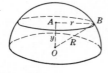

Solution. Let the base of the hemisphere be in the fixed plane. Then A_y is any section parallel to and distant y from this plane. Denote by r the radius of this section. From right triangle OAB, we have

$$r^2 = R^2 - y^2.$$

Therefore

$$A_y = \pi r^2 = \pi R^2 - \pi y^2. \quad Ans.$$

Substituting in this equation $y = \dfrac{R}{2}$, we find the mid-section

$$M = A_{\frac{R}{2}} = \pi R^2 - \pi \left(\frac{R}{2}\right)^2 = \tfrac{3}{4}\pi R^2. \quad Ans.$$

PROBLEMS

1. For each of the following solids verify the value of A_y given and find the area of the mid-section parallel to the base.   The letters U, L, and h in these formulas denote upper base, lower base, and altitude, respectively.

(*a*) Prisms, cylinders. $A_y = L$.

(*b*) Right triangular prism in which an edge is taken as lower base and the opposite face as upper base. $A_y = \dfrac{U(h - y)}{h}$, where y is the distance from the upper base.

(*c*) Pyramid. $A_y = \dfrac{Ly^2}{h^2}$, where y is the distance from the vertex.

(*d*) Cone. $A_y = \dfrac{\pi r^2}{h^2} y^2$, where y is the distance from the vertex.

(*e*) Sphere. $A_y = 2\pi Ry - \pi y^2$, where y is the distance from the plane parallel to the base and tangent to the spherical surface.

(*f*) Frustum of pyramid. $A_y = \left(\dfrac{\sqrt{L} - \sqrt{U}}{h}\right)^2 y^2 - 2\left(\dfrac{L - \sqrt{LU}}{h}\right) y + L$, where y is the distance from the lower base L.

(*g*) Frustum of cone. $A_y = \pi \left[r_1{}^2 + 2r_1(r_2 - r_1)\dfrac{y}{h} + (r_2 - r_1)^2\dfrac{y^2}{h^2} \right]$, where y is the distance from base of radius r_1.

(*h*) Segment of sphere of two bases and of altitude h.
$A_y = \pi \left[b^2 + \dfrac{(a^2 + h^2 - b^2)}{h} y - y^2 \right]$, where y is distance from the base of radius b.

2. Prove that, if in a general prismatoid y is measured from a plane d units from the fixed plane, A_y is still a polynomial in y of not higher than the second degree.   Show also that the coefficient of y^2 is unchanged.

3. If a solid has a square for upper base, a rectangle for lower base, and isosceles trapezoids for faces, find A_y in terms of the distance from the lower base.

4. The bases of a solid are perpendicular to a lateral edge.   The upper base is a right triangle, the lower base is a square, and the faces are triangles and trapezoids.   Find A_y in terms of the distance from the lower base.

43. PRISMATOID THEOREM

The volume of a prismatoid is equal to the algebraic sum of the volumes of a pyramid, a wedge, and a parallelepiped.

Analysis. Consider the prismatoid (see figure) of upper base U, lower base L, and altitude h, for which section

$$A_y = \pm\, ay^2 \pm by + L, \tag{1}$$

where y is the distance from base L. Substituting $y = h$ in (1), we get

$$U = A_h = \pm\, ah^2 \pm bh + L. \tag{2}$$

Now construct a pyramid (see figure) of base $U_1 = ah^2$ and of altitude h; a wedge (right triangular prism standing on lateral edge)

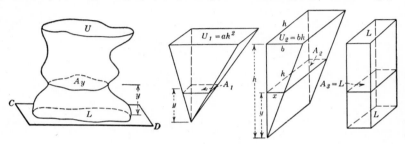

of altitude h and of base b by h; and a parallelepiped of altitude h and of base L. Place these solids so that the vertex of the pyramid, the edge of the wedge, and the lower base of the parallelepiped lie in the plane containing the base L of the prismatoid and bases U_1, U_2, and L lie in the plane of base U as shown. Denote by A_1, A_2, and A_3 the sections cut from the pyramid, wedge, and parallelepiped, respectively, by the plane containing section A_y of the prismatoid.

Considering the pyramid, we have from the theorem for similar figures, §22,

$$\frac{A_1}{U_1} = \frac{y^2}{h^2},$$

or

$$A_1 = \frac{U_1 y^2}{h^2} = \frac{ah^2 y^2}{h^2} = ay^2; \tag{3}$$

and considering the wedge, we have from similar triangles

$$\frac{x}{y} = \frac{b}{h}, \quad \text{or} \quad x = \frac{by}{h}.$$

Therefore

$$A_2 = xh = by. \tag{4}$$

Also we note that

$$A_3 = L. \tag{5}$$

Substituting in (1) $ay^2 = A_1$ from (3), $by = A_2$ from (4), and $L = A_3$ from (5), we have

$$A_y = \pm A_1 \pm A_2 + A_3, \tag{6}$$

whence in accordance with Cavalieri's theorem the volume of a prismatoid is equal to the algebraic sum of the volumes of a pyramid, a wedge, and a parallelepiped, or

$$V = \pm \tfrac{1}{3}ah^3 \pm \tfrac{1}{2}bh^2 + Lh,$$

where $\frac{1}{3}ah^3$ is the volume of the pyramid, $\frac{1}{2}bh^2$ is the volume of the wedge, and Lh is the volume of the parallelepiped.

44. PROOF OF THE PRISMOIDAL FORMULA

In the preceding article we found the volume of the prismatoid to be

$$V = \tfrac{1}{3}ah^3 + \tfrac{1}{2}bh^2 + Lh, \tag{1}$$

where a and b are constants which are positive, negative, or zero. We shall now show that this can be transformed into the familiar prismoidal formula of §30.

Factoring out $h/6$ from the right-hand member of (1) and transforming the resulting terms, we have

$$V = \frac{h}{6}[2ah^2 + 3bh + 6L]$$

$$= \frac{h}{6}[(ah^2 + bh + L) + (ah^2 + 2bh + 4L) + L]$$

$$= \frac{h}{6}\left[(ah^2 + bh + L) + L + 4\left(\frac{ah^2}{4} + \frac{bh}{2} + L\right)\right]$$

$$= \frac{h}{6}\left\{ (ah^2 + bh + L) + L + 4\left[a\left(\frac{h}{2}\right)^2 + b\left(\frac{h}{2}\right) + L\right]\right\}.$$

But since $A_y = ay^2 + by + L$, we have

$$ah^2 + bh + L = A_h = U, \text{ and } a\left(\frac{h}{2}\right)^2 + b\left(\frac{h}{2}\right) + L = A_{\frac{h}{2}} = M.$$

Hence

$$V = \frac{h}{6}\,(U + L + 4M).$$

This remarkable formula may be used, in general, to find not only all the areas and volumes of plane and solid geometry but a great many others besides. It can be used to get a close approximation to most of the physical quantities that are used in engineering science.

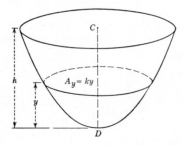

Example 1. The solid shown in the figure has an elliptic base perpendicular to the axis CD and has an altitude h. If the area of any section parallel to the base is proportional to the distance y from the vertex D, that is $A_y = ky$, find the volume of the solid. (This solid is called a segment of an elliptic paraboloid.)

Solution. Since $A_y = ky$, we have

$$L = A_0 = 0, \quad M = A_{\frac{h}{2}} = k\left(\frac{h}{2}\right), \quad \text{and} \quad U = A_h = kh.$$

Substituting these values of L, M, and U in the prismoidal formula, we have

$$V = \frac{h}{6}\left(kh + 0 + \tfrac{1}{2}kh\right) = \tfrac{1}{4}kh^2. \quad Ans.$$

Example 2. A solid has a circular base of diameter R. The line AB is a diameter of the base. Find the volume of the solid if every section perpendicular to AB is a right triangle of base c and altitude mc.

Solution. Let y be the distance from A to section A_y. From the figure we write

$$A_y = \tfrac{1}{2}c(mc) = \frac{mc^2}{2},$$

and from plane geometry (Reference 64, §50) we have

$$\left(\frac{c}{2}\right)^2 = Ry - y^2,$$

or

$$\frac{c^2}{2} = 2Ry - 2y^2.$$

But

$$A_y = \frac{mc^2}{2}.$$

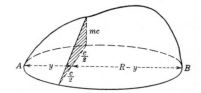

Therefore
$$A_y = 2mRy - 2my^2. \tag{a}$$

Therefore the solid is a prismatoid.

Consider vertices A and B as bases of this solid. Then in the formula

$$V = h \left(\frac{U + L + 4M}{6} \right) \tag{b}$$

$U = 0$ and $L = 0$.

To find the mid-section M substitute $y = R/2$ in (a) to obtain

$$M = A_R = \frac{mR^2}{2}.$$

Whence, substituting these values of U, L, and M in (b), we get

$$V = \tfrac{1}{3}mR^3. \quad Ans.$$

PROBLEMS

1. Find the volume of a general prismatoid (a) whose altitude is 2, and for which $A_y = 15 + 5y - 3y^2$, (b) whose altitude is 3, and for which $A_y = 9y + 4y^2$, where y is the distance from the base of the prismatoid.

2. Find the volume of a sphere of radius R for which $A_y = 2\pi Ry - \pi y^2$, where y is the distance from a plane tangent to the sphere.

3. A segment of one base of a sphere of radius R has an altitude h. Find its volume, using the value of A_y in Prob. 2.

4. Find the volume of a spherical segment of one base if its altitude is h and its base radius is b. See Prob. 1h, §42.

5. Find the volume of the spherical segment of altitude h and of base radii a and b. See Prob. 1h, §42.

6. If R and r are respectively the radii of the larger and smaller bases of the frustum of a cone of altitude h, show that $A_y = \pi \left(r + \dfrac{R - r}{h} y \right)^2$, where y is the distance from the smaller base. Find the volume of the frustum.

7. The segment of a paraboloid of revolution (see figure) is a solid in which every section parallel to the base is a circle the radius of which is the mean proportional between the distance y from the vertex and the radius of the base. Find the volume of the segment of altitude h and base radius b if $h = b$.

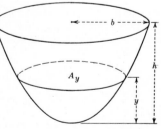

8. Using the prismoidal formula, derive the formula for the volume of each of the following prismatoids: (a) pyramid, (b) cone, (c) sphere, (d) segment of a sphere, (e) frustum of a pyramid.

9. For the solid shown in the figure every section perpendicular to the axis DE is an ellipse of area $A_y = M\left(1 - \dfrac{y^2}{c^2}\right)$, where $M = \pi ab$ is the mid-section, y is the distance of A_y from M, and $c = \frac{1}{2}DE$. Find the volume of the solid. (This solid is called an ellipsoid.)

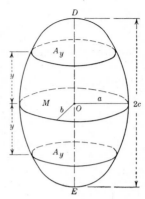

10. In a cone of altitude h and elliptic base B, every section parallel to the base has an area $A_y = \dfrac{By^2}{h^2}$, where y is the distance from the vertex to the section. Find the volume of the cone. (This solid is called an elliptic cone.)

11. For the solid shown in the figure every section perpendicular to the axis DE is an ellipse of area $A_y = \dfrac{2y^2}{h^2}(B - 2M) + (4M - B)\dfrac{y}{h}$, where $B = \pi ab$ is the upper base, M is the mid-section, y is the distance from D to A_y, and $h = DE$ is the altitude. Find the volume of the solid. (This solid is called a segment of an elliptic hyperboloid of two sheets.)

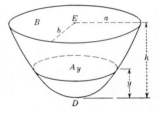

12. For the solid shown in the figure every section perpendicular to the axis DE is an ellipse of area $A_y = (B - M)\dfrac{y^2}{h^2} + M$, where $B = \pi a_1 b_1$ is the area of the upper base as well as that of the lower base, $M = \pi ab$ is the area of the mid-section, y is the distance from O to A_y, and $h = \frac{1}{2}DE$ is one-half the altitude. Find the volume of the solid. (This solid is called a segment of an elliptic hyperboloid of one sheet.)

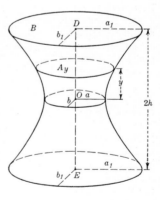

13. A variable rectangle generates a solid by moving from a fixed point and keeping parallel to its first position. One side of the rectangle is equal to the distance the rectangle moves from the fixed point, and the other side is equal to twice this distance. What is the volume generated while the rectangle moves a distance of 2 ft.?

14. A wedge (see Fig.(a)) is cut from a cylinder of radius 5 in. by two planes, one perpendicular to the axis of the cylinder and the other passing through a diameter of the section made by the first plane and inclined to this plane at an angle of 45°. Find the volume of the wedge.

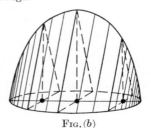

FIG.(a)   FIG.(b)

15. A solid has a circular base of radius 20 in. Find the volume of the solid if every plane section perpendicular to a certain diameter is

(a) an equilateral triangle (see Fig.(b));

(b) an isosceles right triangle with its hypotenuse in the plane of the base;

(c) an isosceles right triangle with one leg in the plane of the base;

(d) an isosceles triangle with its altitude equal to its base;

(e) a square.

16. The base (see figure) of a certain solid is a quarter circle of radius 10 in. Every section parallel to one face is a right triangle, whose altitude is 1.6 times its base. Find its volume.

17. The base of a certain solid is a circle of radius r. If all sections perpendicular to a fixed diameter of the base are (a) squares, (b) isosceles right triangles, find the volume of the solid. (These solids are called conoids.)

18. For the solid shown in Fig.(c) every section perpendicular to edge CD is a circle of diameter $20y - 3y^2$, where y is the distance of the section from C. If the altitude DC of the solid is 4, find its volume.

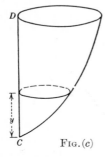

FIG.(c)

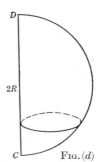

FIG.(d)

19. For the solid shown in Fig.(d) every section perpendicular to edge CD is a circle. If arc CD is a semicircle of diameter $2R$, find the volume of the solid.

20. The base of a certain solid is a triangle of base b and altitude h. If all sections perpendicular to the altitude of the triangle are regular hexagons, find the volume of the solid.

21. Two cylinders (see figure) with circular bases have a common upper base and tangent lower bases. If the radius of each base is 10 in. and if the altitude of each solid is 20 in., find the volume of the part common to the two cylinders.

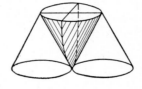

22. The center of a square moves along a diameter of a given circle of radius a, the plane of the square being perpendicular to this diameter, and its magnitude varying in such a way that two opposite vertices move along the circumference of the given circle. Find the volume of the solid generated.

23. Two cylinders (see figure below) of equal radius r have their axes meeting at right angles. Find the volume of the common part.

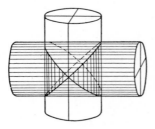

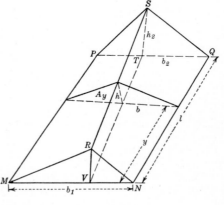

24. Show that the solid represented in the figure is a prismatoid. MQ is a plane and RT is a plane perpendicular to MQ. The warped surfaces MS and RQ are generated by moving straight lines that remain parallel to the base plane MRN.

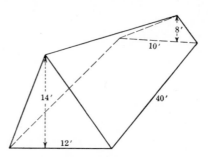

25. Find the volume of the prismatoid shown in the figure.

26. The figure represents a solid cut out of a circular cylinder of radius a and altitude h. O is on the axis of the cylinder, the semicircular base ABD is perpendicular to the axis, and ABC is a plane section. Find the volume of the solid.

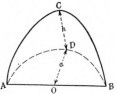

27. By means of the prismoidal formula, derive a formula for the area of a (a) square, (b) rectangle, (c) parallelogram, (d) triangle, (e) trapezoid.

28. By means of the prismoidal formula, derive a formula for the area of the lateral surface of a (a) cube, (b) rectangular parallelepiped, (c) right cylinder, (d) right prism.

45. APPLICATION OF PRISMATOID THEOREM

It is interesting to note that the volume of a prismatoid may be found by direct application of the prismatoid theorem of §43. Thus after finding

$$A_y = ay^2 + by + L$$

we write

$$A_h = ah^2 + bh + L.$$

We may think of the terms in the right-hand member of this equation as the areas of the bases of a pyramid, a wedge, and a parallelepiped, respectively, of common altitude h, and write for the sum of the volumes of these solids

$$V = \tfrac{1}{3}ah^3 + \tfrac{1}{2}bh + Lh.$$

Example. If the area of a section of a prismatoid at a distance y from the base is

$$A_y = 10 - 4y + 6y^2 \text{ sq. in.}$$

and the altitude is 5 in., find the volume.

Solution. Since

$$A_y = 10 - 4y + 6y^2,$$

the volume of the prismatoid may be thought of as the algebraic sum of the volumes of a parallelepiped, a wedge, and a pyramid, with a common altitude h and with bases 10, $(4)(5)$, and $(6)(5)^2$, respectively. Therefore

$$V = (10)(5) - \frac{4(5)^2}{2} + \frac{6(5)^3}{3} = \textbf{250 cu. in.} \quad Ans.$$

PROBLEMS

1. Using the method of this article, solve Probs. 1 to 27 of §44.

2. Prove that the volume of a prismatoid of altitude h is equal to the sum of the volumes of a frustum of a pyramid and a prism each of altitude h.   When is the volume of a prismatoid equal to the volume of the frustum alone?   At what distance from the base of the frustum is the vertex of the pyramid?

Hint.   Write $A_y = ay^2 + by + L = a\left(y + \dfrac{b}{2a}\right)^2 + \left(L - \dfrac{b^2}{4a}\right)$.

3. By means of the calculus (a subject in advanced mathematics), it can be shown that the volume of a solid whose altitude is h and for which $A_y = ay^n$ is equal to the volume of a prism of altitude h and base $\dfrac{ah^{n+1}}{n+1}$.   Using this fact, show that the volume of any solid whose altitude is h and for which $A_y = ay^3 + by^2 + cy + L$ is equal to the sum of the volumes of a prism, pyramid, wedge, and parallelepiped.   Also show that the volume of this solid can be found by the prismoidal formula.

CHAPTER IX

SUMMARY AND REVIEW

46. SUMMARY OF FORMULAS

The following list is a summary of all the formulas we have used in the mensuration of solids.

VOLUMES

Cube   Rectangular Parallelepiped

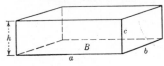

Prism   Cylinder

$Volume = base \times altitude.$

$$V = Bh.$$

Pyramid   Cone

$Volume = \frac{1}{3}\, base \times altitude.$

$$V = \tfrac{1}{3}Bh.$$

Frustums   Prismatoid

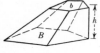

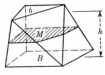

$$V = \frac{(b + B + \sqrt{bB})}{3}\, h.$$

$$V = \frac{(b + B + 4M)}{6}\, h$$

131

Truncated Triangular Prism

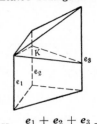

$$V = \frac{e_1 + e_2 + e_3}{3} K.$$

Sphere   **Segments**   **Sector**

$V = \frac{4}{3}\pi R^3.$

$V = \frac{1}{3}\pi h^2\,(3R - h).$
$V = \frac{1}{3}\pi h(3a^2 + 3b^2 + h^2).$

$V = \frac{1}{3}ZR.$

Volumes of revolution

$$V = \left(\frac{\alpha}{360°}\; 2\pi\bar{x}\right) A.$$

$\bar{x}$ = distance from axis to c.g. of area;
α = angle in degrees through which area revolves;
A = generating area.

AREAS

The *total area* of any solid *is* the *sum of* the *areas of* its *bounding surfaces*.
The *lateral area* of a solid *is* its *total area minus* the *area of* its *bases* (or base).

Sphere   **Zone**

$S = 4\pi R^2.$ $Z = 2\pi Rh.$

Surfaces of Revolution

$$S = \left(\frac{\alpha}{360°}\; 2\pi\bar{x}\right) L.$$

$\bar{x}$ = distance from axis to c.g. of curve;
α = angle in degrees through which curve revolves;
L = length of generating curve.

47. REVIEW PROBLEMS

1. Find the weight of a brass water pipe 20 ft. long whose inside diameter is 1.5 in. and whose thickness is $\frac{1}{4}$ in., if brass weighs 520 lb. per cu. ft.

2. The great Chinese wall is said to be 1500 miles long, 20 ft. high, 15 ft. wide at the top, and 25 ft. wide at the bottom. If it were possible to build with this material a wall around the earth at the equator, of a uniform thickness of 4 ft., how high could it be made? (The equator is approximately 24,900 miles long.)

3. Two spheres of lead, of radii 2 and 3 in., respectively, are melted into a cylinder of revolution of radius 1 in. Find the altitude of the cylinder.

4. In Fingal's Cave, on the Island of Staffa (Hebrides, Scotland), the walls are formed by basaltic prismatic columns varying in height from 18 to 36 ft. These columns, mostly hexagonal, are so perfect as to suggest the hand of man. One of the vertical columns is 29.3 ft. in height and has a base of 4.7 sq. ft. What is its volume?

5. If the gravity dam whose cross section is shown in the figure weighs 150 lb. per cu. ft., find the total weight of a section of the dam 50 ft. long.

6. A light is placed 5 ft. from the center of a globe 3 ft. in diameter. Find the area of the illuminated portion.

7. If a piece of brass 8 by 6 by 12 in. is drawn out into a wire $\frac{1}{30}$ in. in diameter, what will be the length of the wire?

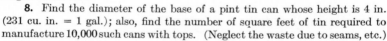

8. Find the diameter of the base of a pint tin can whose height is 4 in. (231 cu. in. = 1 gal.); also, find the number of square feet of tin required to manufacture 10,000 such cans with tops. (Neglect the waste due to seams, etc.)

9. An anchor ring is formed by revolving a circle 2 in. in diameter about a line lying in the plane of the circle and at a distance of 7 in. from its center. Find the volume of the solid formed.

10. How many cubic inches of lumber does a stick contain if it is 4 in. by 4 in. at one end, 2 in. by 2 in. at the other end, and 16 ft. long?

11. Find the waste in cutting the strongest square timber from a circular log of uniform diameter 2 ft. and length 8 ft.

12. The water supply of a district consists of a lake whose surface area is 1000 acres. The number of households supplied with water is 60,000. Supposing each household to use 25 gal. per day, calculate how many days' supply (to the nearest day below the exact number) is represented by a depth of 1 ft. of water in the lake. (1 acre equals 43,560 sq. ft.)

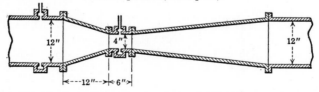

13. The accompanying figure represents the longitudinal view of a Venturi meter, a device designed to measure the flow of water in pipes. If the throat of the meter is 6 in. long and has an inside diameter of 4 in., find the volume of water contained in the meter which is used in a 12-in. pipe line if the altitudes of the tapering parts are in the ratio of 1:3 and the smaller altitude measures 12 in.

14. A concrete surge chamber with circular cross section and vertical inner walls has an inside diameter of 100 ft. The outer walls taper uniformly $\frac{1}{4}$ in. to 1 ft. of rise, and at the base the thickness is 5 ft. The height of the surge chamber is 150 ft. above the pressure tunnel, and the material used in its construction weighs 150 lb. per cu. ft. Find the total weight of the chamber when full of water.

15. A spherical shell 2 in. thick has an outer diameter of 12 in. Find the volume of the material of which it is made.

16. Each of the mammoth dredges used in digging the Panama Canal had a dipper the capacity of which was 15 cu. yd. If the height of this dipper was 10 ft. $9\frac{1}{2}$ in., what was the area of the bottom?

17. Assuming that a city has 400 miles of water pipes and that the average diameter of the pipes is 1 ft., how much water is required to fill this entire system?

18. A stone bridge has three equal semicircular arches resting on four equal rectangular piers. The radius of each arch is R, the dimensions of the piers L, W, H, while the distance from the top of each pier to the top of the bridge is D. If $L = 50$ ft., $W = 5$ ft., $H = 10$ ft., $R = 6$ ft., $D = 12$ ft., find the number of cubic yards of material used in building the bridge.

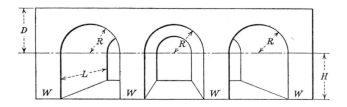

19. A druggist sells a certain kind of powder in a rectangular box 4 by $2\frac{1}{2}$ by $1\frac{1}{4}$ in. for 25 cents, and in a cylindrical can $2\frac{1}{2}$ in. high and $2\frac{1}{2}$ in. in diameter for 10 cents. Which is the more economical buy?

20. A factory chimney has the shape of a frustum of a regular pyramid. Its height is 180 ft., and its upper and lower bases are squares whose sides are 10 ft. and 16 ft., respectively. The cross section of the flue is a square whose side is 7 ft. How many cubic feet of material does the chimney contain?

21. A stone is dropped into a circular tub 40 in. in diameter, causing the water therein to rise 20 in. What is the volume of the stone?

22. How many square feet of tin are required to make a funnel, if the diameters of the top and bottom are 28 in. and 14 in., respectively, and the height is 24 in.?

23. It is desired to cut off a piece of lead pipe 2 in. in outside diameter and $\frac{1}{4}$ in. thick, so that it will melt into a cube of edge 4 in. How long a piece will be required?

24. A pipe of $\frac{3}{4}$-in. inside diameter conducts water from a spring to a house 300 ft. distant. It is desired to empty the pipe after the water has been turned off at the spring. Will a 10-qt. pail hold the water? (One gal. = 231 cu. in.)

25. A reservoir 10 ft. deep is in the form of the frustum of an inverted square pyramid with bases 100 and 90 ft. on a side, respectively. How long will it require an inlet pipe to fill this reservoir if the water pours in at the rate of 200 gal. per min.? (One gal. = 231 cu. in.)

26. A wooden ball 2 ft. in diameter weighs 200 lb. Find the diameter of a ball of the same material which weighs 50 lb.

27. One hundred and fifty posts are used in fencing a lawn. Each post is built in the form of a frustum of a pyramid surmounted by a pyramid whose lower base is common with the upper base of the frustum. The height of the pyramidal top is 2 in. and the common base is a square 4 in. on an edge. The lower base of the frustum has an edge of 6 in. If the overall height of each is 6 ft., how much concrete will be used in making the posts?

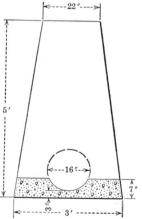

28. A water tank, open at the top, consists of a right circular cylinder and a right circular cone, as shown. If the altitude of the cylinder is three times its radius, and the altitude of the cone is two times the same radius, find the number of square feet of sheet metal required to construct a tank having a capacity of 10,000 gal. (One gal. = 231 cu. in.)

29. A certain Chinese coin, $\frac{1}{2}$ in. in diameter and $\frac{1}{16}$ in. thick, is pierced by a square hole which is $\frac{1}{8}$ in. on a side. Find the amount of metal in the coin.

30. Window glass formerly was made by gathering a lump of molten glass on the end of a hollow rod and blowing it into the form of a large hollow cylinder about 6 ft. long and $1\frac{1}{2}$ ft. in diameter. This was cut longitudinally and then placed in an oven and heated until it softened, when it was flattened out into plates and cut into the desired sizes. If this plate was 0.12 in. thick, find the amount of glass in the original lump.

31. One section of the mainline sewer pipe for the city of Annapolis passes through a tunnel 484 ft. long. The cross section of the tunnel is shown in the figure. The sewer pipe is 16 in. in external diameter and is partially imbedded, in a mattress of concrete, a cross section of which is shown in the figure. Find the total cost (a) of digging the tunnel at $5.00 per cubic yard, (b) of pouring the concrete at $9.00 per cubic yard.

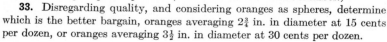

32. A coffee pot is 5 in. deep, $4\frac{1}{2}$ in. in diameter at the top, and $5\frac{3}{4}$ in. in diameter at the bottom. How many cups of coffee will it hold if 6 cups equal a quart? (Answer to nearest whole number.)

33. Disregarding quality, and considering oranges as spheres, determine which is the better bargain, oranges averaging $2\frac{3}{4}$ in. in diameter at 15 cents per dozen, or oranges averaging $3\frac{1}{2}$ in. in diameter at 30 cents per dozen.

34. The inside of a vase is an inverted cone 2.983 in. across the top and 5.016 in. deep. If a heavy sphere 2.498 in. in diameter is dropped into it when the vase is full of water, how much water will overflow?

35. In the foundation work of the Woolworth Building, a 55-story building in New York City, it was necessary, in order to reach bedrock, to penetrate the sand and quicksand to a depth, in some instances, of 131 ft. If the largest circular caisson, 19 ft. in diameter, was 130 ft. deep and was filled with concrete to within 30 ft. of the surface, how many cubic yards of concrete were required?

36. A hole 6 in. in diameter was bored through a sphere 10 in. in diameter. Find the volume of the part cut out.

37. A factory chimney is in the form of a frustum of a regular square pyramid. The chimney is 120 ft. high and the edges of its bases are 12 ft. and 8 ft., respectively. The cross section of the flue is 6 ft. square. How many cubic feet of material does the chimney contain?

38. A log 18 ft. long is 2 ft. in diameter at the top end and 3 ft. in diameter at the butt end.

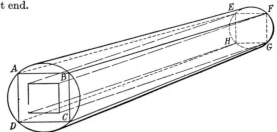

(a) How many cubic feet of wood does the log contain?

(b) How many cubic feet are there in the largest piece of timber of square cross section that can be cut from the log?

(c) How many cubic feet are in the largest piece of square timber the same size throughout its whole length?

(d) How many board feet does the piece of timber in (c) contain, a board foot being equivalent to a board 1 ft. square and 1 in. thick?

Hint. In (b) the larger end is the square *ABCD*. What is the smaller end? In (c) one end is the square *EFGH*. What is the other end?

39. A grain elevator in the form of a frustum of a right circular cone is 24 ft. high, and the radii of its bases are 10 ft. and 5 ft., respectively; how many bushels of wheat will it hold if $1\frac{1}{4}$ cu. ft. equals 1 bu.?

40. When a liquid freezes, it changes into a mass of solid bodies, each of which has a definite geometric form and is known as a crystal. Crystals are always bounded by plane surfaces, which are arranged in an orderly fashion with reference to imaginary lines drawn through the crystal and called its axes. Every crystal has therefore a definite geometric form. Compare the volumes of two crystals, one in the shape of a hexagonal right prism *a* units on a side and 2*a* units in altitude, and the other in the shape of two oppositely directed hexagonal regular pyramids, each *a* units high with a common base *a* units on a side.

41. Soap kettles used in the commercial manufacture of soap are as a rule large cylindrical vats, 500,000 lb. or more of soap being made in a single heating. Find the capacity of such a kettle having an inside diameter of 18 ft. and an altitude of 30 ft. if soap weighs 70 lb. per cu. ft.

42. From a cylindrical glass 6 in. high and 3 in. in diameter, water is poured by tilting the glass until the highest point of the bottom of the glass lies in the plane of the water surface. How much water remains?

43. Imagine a cube to measure 5 units on an edge, and to have its total surface area painted blue. Without the aid of a figure or a cubical object, answer the following questions.

(*A*) How many times must you cut completely through the cube to make cubes which measure 1 unit on an edge?

(*B*) How many of the cubes of question (*A*) will have:

    (*a*) Three blue faces?   (*c*) One blue face?

    (*b*) Two blue faces?   (*d*) No blue face?

(*C*) How many cubes are there in all?

44. The silo shown in the sketch is an air- and water-tight tower. It consists of a lower cylinder surmounted by a frustum of a cone whose lower base is the upper base of the cylinder. The frustum in turn is surmounted by a cupola consisting of a smaller cylinder whose lower base is the upper base of the frustum. This smaller cylinder is topped by a conical roof. The inside radii of the smaller and larger cylinders are 6 ft. and 12 ft., respectively. The altitudes of the frustum and larger cylinder are 6 ft. and 21 ft., respectively. If ensilage can be stored up to the cupola, find the storage capacity of the silo.

45. From a cylindrical jar 4 in. high and 6 in. in diameter, water is poured by tilting the jar until the center of the bottom is at the surface of the water. A plane is passed through the water parallel to both the axis of the jar and the wetted diameter. What is the section made by this plane with the water? If the plane had been passed perpendicular to the wetted diameter, what would be the section?

46. A reservoir is in the form of a frustum of a cone, 68 ft. across the top, 35 ft. across the bottom, and 18 ft. deep. Find the cost of lining it with tile at $1 per square foot.

47. Powder grains manufactured for use in large guns are small cylinders (composed of a nitrocellulose compound) with a number of longitudinal perforations. If each grain is $\frac{3}{4}$ in. in diameter, $1\frac{1}{4}$ in. long, and contains 7 cylindrical perforations $\frac{1}{8}$ in. in diameter, find the amount of material in a single grain.

48. A concrete dam of height 128 ft. was built in a gorge. One side *AB* of the gorge slopes at an angle of 60°, the other side *CD* at 45°. The bases of the dam are horizontal and rec- 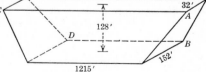 tangular in shape. The lower base is 1215 ft. by 152 ft., and the upper base is 32 ft. wide. How many cubic yards of concrete were required?

49. A tin cup is in the shape of a frustum of a cone. The internal diameters of the cup at the top and bottom are respectively 3 in. and 4 in., and the internal depth is 6 in. Suppose that a conical piece is added to the cup so as to complete the cone. Find the height of the whole cone and the volume of the cone in pints.

50. Find the weight of a copper wire $\frac{1}{8}$ in. in diameter and 2 miles long. Allow 550 lb. of copper to a cubic foot.

51. The volume of a sphere is 86.5 cu. in.; find the volume and surface of a cube inscribed in it.

52. A flat-bottomed boat 10 ft. long and 2 ft. wide is to have vertical sides and ends, of such a height that the boat will float with half of each side above water when the total load including the boat's weight is 500 lb. Neglecting the thickness of the wood, find, to the nearest inch, what width of plank must be used for making the sides of the boat. Find what weight of water would fill the boat, if a cubic foot of water weighs 62.4 lb.

53. A large rectangular-shaped barge floats in a river, and a mark is made on the side at the level of the water. The barge is 16 ft. long by 7 ft. broad. When a load of gravel is emptied into the barge, the barge sinks $4\frac{1}{2}$ in. Find the weight of the load of gravel. (The sides of the barge are made of comparatively thin wood, and the effect of the immersion of the sides an extra $4\frac{1}{2}$ in. may be neglected.)

54. A log of American cedar, whose specific gravity is 0.55, floats in water. Assume that its bulk is 60 cu. ft. What is its weight? What volume of water does it displace? What part of the volume of the wood is out of water?

55. A cylindrical drum of gasoline is 16 in. high and $11\frac{1}{4}$ in. in diameter (internal measurements). What is the weight of gasoline in it when full? (Gasoline weighs 0.71 times as much as water.)

56. A cylindrical tub of diameter 18 in. has water standing in it to a depth of 9 in. If the height of the tub (internal measurement) is 18 in., what is the volume of the empty part? If this space were filled with a substance which weighed 0.05 lb. per cu. in., what would be the weight of the substance?

57. A hollow buoy is made of sheet steel and its dimensions are those shown in the figure. The base of the buoy is part of a sphere, and the upper portion is a cone tangent to the sphere. The steel is $\frac{3}{8}$ in. thick and weighs 480 lb. per cu. ft. Assume that the dimensions are mean values between the internal and the external, and find the weight of the buoy.

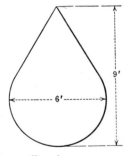

58. If a match box has inside dimensions of 2 in. by $1\frac{1}{4}$ in. by $\frac{5}{8}$ in., find the useful capacity of the box. The cover is made with open ends so that the box can slide into it, the fit being snug. If the match box and cover are made of thin slices of wood $\frac{1}{32}$ in. thick, find the amount of wood used in one million boxes.

59. A triangular prism is used to disperse a beam of white light into a band of different colors, which is known as a spectrum. If the bases of the prism are equilateral triangles 1 in. on a side and the altitude of the prism is 3 in., find the volume of the prism.

60. A wheat elevator in the form of a frustum of a square pyramid is 28 ft. high; the edges of its bases are 12.5 ft. and 6 ft., respectively. How many bushels of wheat will it hold? (One bushel = $1\frac{1}{4}$ cu. ft.)

61. A stone wall is 47 ft. long. One end is 3 ft. high, 2 ft. thick at the top, and 3 ft. thick at the bottom. The other end is 9 ft. high, 2 ft. thick at

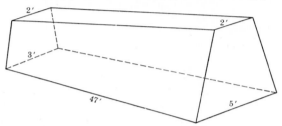

the top, and 5 ft. thick at the bottom. Find the volume of the wall if the ends lie in parallel planes.

62. How many cubic feet of water are in a pond covering 200 acres if its average depth is 20 ft.?

63. If a bell 4 in. in height, 3 in. in external diameter, and $\frac{1}{4}$ in. thick weighs 2 lb., what should be the dimensions of a bell of the same proportions that would weigh 2000 lb.?

64. If a man can dig a small cellar in the form of a cube 5 ft. on an edge in one day, how long will it take him to dig a similar cellar 10 ft. on an edge?

65. The solid shown in the figure has parallel triangular bases ABC and DEF. All face angles at B and E are 90°. Find its volume.

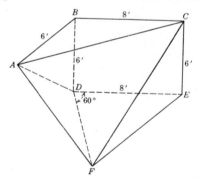

66. The area of the total surface of a polyhedron weighing 64 lb. is 340 sq. in. What is the surface of a similar polyhedron made of the same material and weighing 1000 lb.?

67. A cubic inch of gold is beaten into gold leaf sufficient to cover 7 sq. ft. Find the thickness of the gold leaf.

68. The thickness of a metal spherical shell is t in. and its mean radius is r in. Show that the volume of the metal is $\pi t\left(4r^2 + \dfrac{t^2}{3}\right)$ cu. in.

69. A circular area of radius a moves perpendicular to and with its center on the semicircumference of an equal circle. Find the volume of the solid it will generate.

70. Find the surface generated by revolving about the line AB the area shown in the figure. CDE is a semicircle.

71. Find the diameter of a gun which fires a shell weighing twice as much as a shell fired from an 8-in. gun, supposing the shells to be geometrically similar.

72. If the shells used in guns are similar in shape, find the ratio of the total surface areas of an 8-in. and a 12-in. shell.

73. A chain 100 ft. 2 in. long has circular links made from an iron rod 1 in. in diameter. If each link has an internal diameter of 6 in., compute the weight of the chain, assuming the weight of iron to be 450 lb. per cu. ft.

74. The plane area $ABCD$ (see figure) is revolved about the line YY'. Find the surface and volume generated, using (a) the theorems of Pappus and (b) the formulas for the lateral area and volume of a frustum of a right circular cone.

75. A chimney 65 ft. high is 4 ft. in diameter at the top and 10 ft. in diameter at the bottom. The flue is 2 ft. in diameter at the top and 4 ft. in diameter at the bottom. Find the weight of the chimney in tons if the masonry weighs 142 lb. per cu. ft.

76. Find the surface and volume of a sphere circumscribed about a cylinder of revolution, the radius of whose base is 3 in. and whose altitude is 8 in.

77. With the vertices of an equilateral triangle of side 10 in. as centers and radii equal to 5 in., three arcs are described within the triangle. Taking the figure bounded by these arcs as the base of a right cylinder, find the volume and total area of the cylinder if its altitude is 12 in.

Solve this problem if the arcs are described outside the triangle.

78. A square and an equilateral triangle having their bases parallel are inscribed in a circle of radius R; the whole figure is then revolved about the diameter AB perpendicular to the base of the triangle. Find, in terms of R, (a) the total area of each of the three surfaces generated, (b) the volume of each of the three solids generated.

79. The center of a sphere of radius R lies in the surface of a sphere of radius $2R$. Find (a) the volume common to the two solids, (b) the volume of the combined solid, (c) the volume of a third sphere whose volume equals the volume of the solid of (b).

80. A steel buoy consists of a spherical segment and a cone having a common base of radius 3 ft. The altitude of the segment is 2 ft. and that of the cone is 6 ft. Find the total surface of the buoy.

81. A tin pan 2 ft. high, with a spherical bottom, has its sides flared out 60° from the vertical. The bottom measures 4 ft. across. How much tin, neglecting the seams, does it take to make it? The sides are tangent to the bottom.

82. A right circular cone whose vertical angle is 90° has the diameter of a sphere as its axis and has its vertex on the sphere. Show that one-fourth of the sphere lies outside the cone.

83. The Washington Monument took $36\frac{1}{2}$ years to complete, at a cost of $1,130,000. This tremendous structure has an overall height of 555 ft. and consists of the frustum of a pyramid whose lower base is a square 55 ft. on a side, and whose four faces slope inward 0.247 in. horizontally to a rise of 1 ft. The frustum is surmounted by a hollow pyramid having the same base as the upper base of the frustum. The altitude of the pyramid is 55 ft. and its sides are constructed of solid marble 7 in. thick. The frustum in turn is hollowed out along its entire axis by an opening whose cross section is a square. The sides of the opening rise vertically upward from the base 150 ft. At this level there is an offset outward from the vertical of $3\frac{1}{2}$ ft. in a rise of 10 ft., and thereafter the opening continues to have vertical sides to the upper base of the frustum. If the thickness of the sides of the monument at the base is 15 ft., find how much stone was used in its construction.

84. The pyramidal solid $ABCD$ was cut off the corner of a cube. Planes were passed parallel to the base ABC, dividing the edge AD into segments

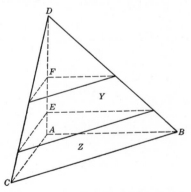

$AE = 1$ in., $EF = 2$ in., and $FD = 3$ in. Find the ratio of the volume of frustum Y to that of frustum Z.

85. A right circular cone of altitude r and radius of base R has its vertex at the center of a sphere of radius r. (a) Derive an expression for the volume which is common to the two solids. (b) Given $r = 3$, $R = 4$, compute the volume.

86. Four grapefruit (considered spheres) 4 in. in diameter are placed in a square box whose inside base dimensions are 8 in.   In the space between the first four grapefruit a fifth of the same diameter is placed.   How deep must the box be in order that the top will just touch the fifth grapefruit?

87. The cube shown in the figure is 3 in. on an edge.   Each of the points A, B is 1 in. from the vertex nearest it. Pass two planes through edge KL, one containing point A and the other containing point B.   Find the volume of the wedge cut from the cube by these two planes.

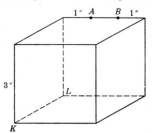

★ **88.** A rod 3 ft. long is suspended from the ceiling in a horizontal position by two equal vertical strings 5 ft. long attached to its ends.   The rod is then rotated through an angle of 90°, remaining horizontal, so that its center C rises in a vertical line.   Find the distance that C rises and the angle that each string then makes with its original position.

89. Find the total area and the volume generated by revolving the circular sector OCD (see figure) about the diameter AB.

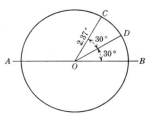

90. A cylindrical glass of radius 1.5 in. and altitude 6 in. is filled with water to a depth of 2 in.   If two balls each 2 in. in diameter are dropped into the glass, by how much is the level of the water raised?

91. In the solid shown in the figure all face angles at A, B, and C are 90°. (*a*) Find the volume of this solid.   ★(*b*) If the 30° angle is changed to 20° find the volume of the solid.

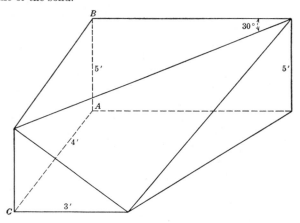

★ **92.** A circular sector of radius 5 in. and angle 110° is bent into the form of a right circular cone.   Find the height and the semivertical angle of the cone.

★ **93.** A homogeneous sphere of radius 6 in. (see figure) is suspended by a string 9 in. long from a point A in a smooth vertical wall AD. Find angle BAD.

Hint. AB produced passes through the center of the sphere.

★ **94.** Solve Prob. 89 if the central angle of the sector OCD is 36° 30′.

★ **95.** Find the area of the earth's surface within the Arctic Circle; that is, in latitude north of 66° 32′ N.

★ **96.** Spherical balls $1\frac{1}{2}$ in. in diameter are packed in a box measuring 6 in. by 3 in. by 3 in. If as many balls as possible are packed in the box, how much free space remains in the box?

★ **97.** A solid consists of a hemisphere surmounted by a cone as shown in the figure. Find the vertical angle of the cone if the volumes of the conical and spherical portions are equal.

★ **98.** A square area of edge a revolves about a line through one vertex, making an angle θ with an edge and not crossing the square. Show that the volume generated is $\pi a^3(\sin\theta + \cos\theta)$.

★ **99.** A chemists' measuring glass is conical in shape. If it is 8 c.m. deep and 3 c.m. across the mouth, find the distance on the slant edge between the markings for 1 c.c. and 2 c.c.

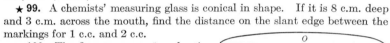

★ **100.** The figure represents a hemispherical bowl of radius 8 in., containing water to a depth of 3 in. Find (*a*) angle POQ, (*b*) the area of the wetted surface, (*c*) the volume of the sector of the sphere whose base is the wetted surface, (*d*) the volume of the cone of vertex O and base PQ, (*e*) the volume of the water in the bowl.

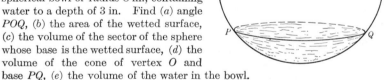

★ **101.** From a point on the ground in a square courtyard of area a^2 the angles of elevation of three flagstaffs of equal height at three consecutive corners of the yard are 60°, 60°, and 45°. Show that the height of each flagstaff is $a\sqrt{3(1 - \frac{1}{2}\sqrt{2})}$.

★ **102.** A plane hillside is inclined at an angle of 28° with the horizontal. A man wearing skis can climb this hillside by following a straight path inclined at an angle of 12° to the horizontal, but one without skis must follow a path inclined at an angle of only 5° with the horizontal. Find the angle between the directions of the two paths.

★ **103.** A billiard ball, aimed at a point A on the edge of the cushion of a horizontal billiard table, rolls along a line making 18° with the cushion. If the cushion overhangs so that its edge is 4 c.m. above the table and if the diameter of the ball is 5 c.m., find the distance (measured along the edge of the cushion) between the point A and the point where the ball strikes the cushion.

★ **104.** A fly stationed at a point on the circumference of the base of a cylindrical tower of radius 12 ft. finds that he can just see a distant flagstaff by walking along the tangent line to the base either a distance 8 ft. in one direction or a distance 5 ft. in the other direction. Find the distance of the foot of the flagstaff from the center of the base of the tower.

APPENDIX

48. A THEOREM ON LIMITS

If two variables are always equal and each approaches a limit, the limits are equal.

Analysis. Let x and y be two variables which are always equal, let a and b be their respective limits, and let u and v be the respective differences between the variables and their limits. The vari-

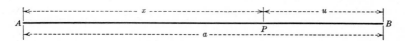

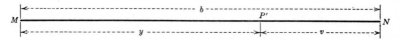

ables x and y can be represented graphically as the distances of two moving points P and P' from two fixed points A and M, as indicated in the figure.

Then from the figure it is clear that

$$x + u = a, \qquad y + v = b;$$

or

$$x = a - u, \qquad y = b - v.$$

But, by hypothesis, $x = y$. Hence

$$a - u = b - v.$$

Therefore

$$a - b = u - v.$$

Now as x approaches a as a limit and y approaches b as a limit, the differences u and v become and remain smaller than any value that can be assigned. Hence the difference $u - v$ becomes and remains smaller than any value that can be assigned.

Since a and b are constants, the difference $a - b$ is also a constant. Hence $u - v$, which is equal to $a - b$, is also a constant.

Since $u - v$ is constant and becomes less than any value that can be assigned, it must be zero.   Hence

$$a - b = 0, \quad \text{or} \quad a = b.$$

Therefore limit of $x =$ limit of y.

49. PROOF OF CAVALIERI'S THEOREM

If, in two solids of equal altitude, the sections made by planes parallel to and at the same distance from their respective bases are always equal, the volumes of the solids are equal.

In proving this theorem we shall assume that, if a plane surface of area B is moved a distance h in a direction perpendicular to itself, it generates a solid of volume Bh.   We shall call this solid an *elemental solid.*

Analysis.   Let the two solids P and Q (see figure) rest on the same horizontal plane, and let their common altitude H be divided into n equal parts each equal to h.   Through the points of division of the altitude pass planes parallel to the horizontal plane of the bases.   These planes will intersect the two solids in sections S_1, S_2, . . . S_{n-1} parallel to the bases and distant h apart.

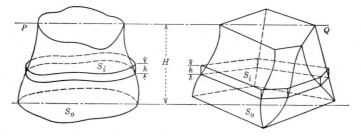

On the bases S_0 of P and Q, and on each of the parallel sections S_1, S_2, . . . S_{n-1} as bases, construct elemental solids of height h. Typical corresponding elemental solids are shown in the figure. Then the volume of each elemental solid will be h times the area of its base S_i.

Denote by P' the volume of the elemental solids belonging to solid P, and by Q' the volume of the elemental solids belonging to Q.   Then since the bases of corresponding elemental solids in P and Q are equal by hypothesis, and they have the same altitude h, their volumes are equal.   Therefore, since the number of elemental solids is the same in P and Q, we have

$$P' = Q'.$$

Now suppose the number of subdivisions n to be increased indefinitely, thereby increasing the number of elemental solids indefinitely and decreasing their altitudes h in a corresponding manner. It is evident that P' will approach P as a limit, and Q' will approach Q as a limit. But P' and Q' are two variables which are always equal. Hence by the theorem of limits of §48 their limits must be equal. Therefore

$$P = Q.$$

Note. The Italian mathematician Bonaventura Cavalieri (1598–1647) first used the theorem, which bears his name, for cases of plane figures. That is, he stated the theorem in such a way as to include not only the volumes of certain solids but also the areas of certain plane figures.

50. REFERENCES FROM PLANE GEOMETRY

DEFINITIONS

1. Altitude of a Triangle. An altitude of a triangle is a perpendicular from any vertex to the side opposite, produced if necessary.

2. Angle. A plane angle is the opening between two straight lines drawn from the same point.

3. Apothem. The apothem of a polygon is the radius of its inscribed circle.

4. Area. The area of a plane figure is the number which expresses the ratio between its surface and the surface of the unit square.

5. Center of Polygon. The center of a regular polygon is the common center of its inscribed and circumscribed circles.

6. Circle. A circle is a closed plane curve every point of which is equally distant from a point in the plane of the curve.

7. Complementary Angles. Two angles are called complementary when their sum is equal to a right angle; and each is called the complement of the other.

8. Concurrent Lines. Three or more lines which have one point in common are said to be concurrent.

9. Definition of π. The number π (pronounced pī), used in calculations on the circle, is the number obtained by dividing the circumference of a circle by its diameter; that is, $\pi = C/D$. Hence, $C = \pi D$ or $C = 2\pi r$. $\pi = 3.1416$ (to 4 decimal places).

10. Diagonal. A diagonal of a polygon is a line joining any two nonconsecutive vertices.

11. Hypotenuse. The hypotenuse of a right triangle is the side opposite the right angle.

12. Isosceles Triangle. An isosceles triangle is a triangle which has two equal sides.

13. Locus. A locus is a figure containing all the points, and only those points, which fulfill a given requirement.

14. Parallel Lines. Parallel lines are lines that lie in the same plane and do not meet however far they are produced.

15. Parallelogram. A parallelogram is a quadrilateral whose opposite sides are parallel.

16. Perpendicular. If one straight line cuts another so as to make any two adjacent angles equal, each line is perpendicular to the other.

17. Quadrilateral. A quadrilateral is a portion of a plane bounded by four straight lines.

18. Rectangle. A rectangle is a parallelogram whose angles are right angles.

19. Regular Polygon. A regular polygon is a polygon all of whose angles are equal and all of whose sides are equal.

20. Similar Polygons. Two polygons are similar if their corresponding angles are equal and their corresponding sides are proportional.

21. Supplementary Angles. One angle is the supplement of another if their sum equals two right angles (or 180°).

22. Tangent. A tangent to a circle is a straight line which, however far it may be produced, has only one point in common with the circle.

23. Trapezoid. A trapezoid is a quadrilateral two and only two of whose sides are parallel.

24. Triangle. A triangle is a portion of a plane bounded by three straight lines.

25. Vertical Angles. When two angles have the same vertex, and the sides of one are the prolongations of the sides of the other, they are called vertical angles.

Theorems

Properties of Triangles

26. The sum of the three angles of a triangle is equal to two right angles.

27. The sum of two sides of a triangle is greater than the third side, and their difference is less than the third side.

28. If two sides of a triangle are unequal, the angles opposite are unequal, and the greater angle is opposite the greater side; and conversely.

29. If two sides of a triangle are equal (an isosceles triangle), the angles opposite these sides are equal; and conversely.

30. The perpendicular bisectors of the sides, and the bisectors of the angles of a triangle, meet in points which are the centers of the circumscribed circle and the inscribed circle, respectively.

31. The altitudes of a triangle meet in a point.

32. The medians of a triangle are concurrent at a point which is two-thirds of the distance from any vertex to the midpoint of the opposite side.

33. Two triangles are congruent if two angles and the included side of the one are equal, respectively, to two angles and the included side of the other.

34. Two triangles are congruent if two sides and the included angle of the one are equal, respectively, to two sides and the included angle of the other.

35. Two triangles are congruent if the three sides of the one are equal, respectively, to the three sides of the other.

Right Triangles

36. Theorem of Pythagoras. In any right triangle the square of the hypotenuse is equal to the sum of the squares of the other two sides.

37. Two right triangles are equal if a side and the hypotenuse of the one are equal, respectively, to a side and the hypotenuse of the other.

38. Two right triangles are equal if the hypotenuse and an adjacent angle of one are equal, respectively, to the hypotenuse and an adjacent angle of the other.

39. If a perpendicular is drawn from the vertex of the right angle to the hypotenuse of a right triangle: (1) the two triangles formed are similar to each other and to the given triangle; (2) the perpendicular is a mean proportional between the segments of the hypotenuse; and (3) the square of either side about the right angle equals the product of the whole hypotenuse and the segment adjacent to that side.

Similar Triangles

40. Two triangles are similar if the angles of one are respectively equal to the angles of the other; or if two angles of one are respectively equal to two angles of the other.

41. Two triangles are similar if an angle of one equals an angle of the other and the sides including these angles are proportional.

42. Two triangles are similar if their sides are in the same ratio.

43. If two triangles have their sides respectively parallel, or respectively perpendicular, each to each, they are similar.

Polygons

44. The sum of the angles of a convex polygon of n sides is $2(n - 2)$ right angles.

45. The exterior angles of a polygon, made by producing each of its sides in succession, are together equal to four right angles.

46. Homologous parts of congruent figures are equal.

Lines

47. If three or more parallels intercept equal parts on one transversal, they intercept equal parts on every transversal.

48. If two parallel lines are cut by a transversal, the alternate interior angles are equal, the exterior-interior angles are equal, and the interior angles on the same side of the transversal are supplementary.

49. If two angles have their sides respectively parallel, or respectively perpendicular, they are either equal or supplementary.

50. If a line is perpendicular to one of two parallel lines it is perpendicular to the other also.

51. Any point in the perpendicular bisector of a line is equally distant from the extremities of the line.

52. Two points each equally distant from the extremities of a line determine the perpendicular bisector of the line.

Parallelograms

53. The opposite sides of a parallelogram are equal, and so also are the opposite angles.

54. The diagonals of a parallelogram bisect each other.

55. If two sides of a quadrilateral are equal and parallel, then the other two sides are equal and parallel, and the figure is a parallelogram.

Circles

56. Through three points not in a straight line one circle, and only one, can be drawn.

57. A tangent to a circle is perpendicular to the radius at the point of tangency; and conversely.

58. The tangents to a circle drawn from an external point are equal, and make equal angles with the line joining the point to the center.

59. An inscribed angle is measured by one-half the intercepted arc.

60. An angle inscribed in a semicircle is a right angle.

61. An angle formed by two chords intersecting within the circle is measured by half the sum of the intercepted arcs.

62. An angle included by a tangent and a chord drawn from the point of contact is measured by half the intercepted arc.

63. An angle formed by two secants, two tangents, or a tangent and a secant, drawn to a circle from an external point, is measured by half the difference of the intercepted arcs.

64. If two chords intersect in a circle, the product of the segments of one is equal to the product of the segments of the other.

65. If from a point outside a circle a secant and a tangent are drawn, the tangent is the mean proportional between the whole secant and its external segment.

66. A perpendicular from a point on the circumference to a diameter of a circle is a mean proportional between the segments of the diameter.

67. The circumferences of two circles are in the same ratio as their radii, and the arcs of two circles subtended by equal central angles are in the same ratio as their radii.

Loci

68. The locus of points equidistant from the sides of a given angle is the bisector of the angle.

69. The perpendicular bisector of a given line is the locus of points equidistant from the extremities of the line.

TABLES

51. EXPLANATION OF TABLE I

To find the logarithm of a number. In general, a four-place table of logarithms gives the mantissas of all integral numbers lying between 99 and 1000. The first two digits of the numbers are found in the left-hand column N, while the third digit is in the row at the top of the page. Therefore the mantissa of a number with three significant figures is in the row with the first two significant figures of the number and in the column headed by the third.

Example 1. Find log 42.4.

Solution. The characteristic is 1. To find the mantissa, first find 42 in the left-hand column headed N, then follow the row containing 42 until the column headed by 4 is reached. Here we find 6274. Therefore the mantissa is .6274. Hence

$$\log 42.4 = \mathbf{1.6274.} \quad Ans.$$

If the significant part of the number consists of less than three digits, annex zeros until you have three digits.

Example 2. Find log 0.041.

Solution. The characteristic is 8. $\quad$ — 10. Using 410, we find the mantissa to be .6128. Therefore

$$\log 0.0410 = \mathbf{8.6128 - 10.} \quad Ans.$$

Interpolation. From the four-place table of logarithms we cannot obtain directly the logarithm of a number with four significant figures. However, by a process known as interpolation, we may find the mantissa of a number having a fourth significant figure. In this process we use the principle of proportional parts which states that, for small changes in N, the corresponding changes in $\log N$ are proportional to the changes in N. While this principle is not strictly true, it is sufficiently accurate to lead to results correct to the number of figures given in the table.

The expression *tabular difference* will be used in what follows. The tabular difference, when used in connection with a table, means the result of subtracting the lesser of two successive entries from the greater.

The process of interpolation is illustrated by means of the following example:

Example.   Find log 235.4.

Solution.   From the table of logarithms we find the logarithms in the following form and then compute the differences exhibited.

$$\left.\begin{array}{l} \log 235.0 \\ \log 235.4 \\ \log 236.0 \end{array}\right\} \begin{array}{l} 4 \\ 10 \end{array} \left.\begin{array}{l} = 2.3711 \\ = ? \\ = 2.3729 \end{array}\right\} x \left.\vphantom{\begin{array}{l} = 2.3711 \\ = ? \\ = 2.3729 \end{array}}\right\} 18 \text{ (tabular difference)}$$

By the principle of proportional parts, we have

$$\frac{4}{10} = \frac{x}{18}, \quad \text{or} \quad x = \left(\frac{4}{10}\right)(18) = 7 \text{ (nearly)}.$$

We add $x = 7$ to the last figure of 2.3711 to obtain

$$\log 235.4 = 2.3718. \quad Ans.$$

Notice that the value used for x was 7 instead of 7.2 because the table of logarithms is accurate only to four decimal places.

The essence of the process of interpolation is indicated in the foregoing procedure.   When the tabular difference is small, this process can easily be performed mentally.   However, the student may interpolate by using the columns headed d and the proportional parts columns (see pp. 156 and 157).

Each entry in the column headed d gives the difference of the logarithms between which it is spaced.   (Obviously each entry in the extreme right-hand column headed d is the difference between the logarithm to the left of it and the first logarithm in the next row.   Thus the difference between the logarithms 0374 and 0414 is found in the column headed d to the right of 0374.)   In each column headed by *Proportional Parts* appears $\frac{0}{10}$, $\frac{1}{10}$, $\frac{2}{10}$, ... $\frac{10}{10}$ of the number heading the column.   Hence the difference $x = 7$ to be applied in the foregoing example is found in the proportional parts column headed by 18 (the tabular difference written between 3711 and 3729) and in the row with the 4 of the column headed t.

To find the number corresponding to a given logarithm.   Generally in every problem involving logarithms, it is necessary not only to find the logarithms of numbers but also to perform the inverse process, that of finding a number corresponding to a given logarithm.

If $\log N = L$, then N is the number corresponding to the logarithm L.   The number N is called the antilogarithm of L.   To find the antilogarithm N of the logarithm L, first use the given mantissa to find the sequence of figures in N, and then use the given characteristic to place the decimal point.

Example.   Given log $N = 1.5248$, find N.

Solution.   The mantissa .5248 is not found exactly in the table, but we find the two successive mantissas .5237 and .5250 between which the given mantissa lies.   From the table we find the numbers in the following form and then compute the differences exhibited.

$$\left.\begin{array}{l} 1.5237 \\ 1.5248 \\ 1.5250 \end{array}\right\} \begin{array}{l} 11 \\ \end{array} \left.\begin{array}{l} \\ 13 \\ \end{array}\right\} \begin{array}{l} = \log 33.40 \\ = \log N \\ = \log 33.50 \end{array} \left.\begin{array}{l} \\ \end{array}\right\} t \left.\begin{array}{l} \\ \\ \end{array}\right\} 10$$

By the principle of proportional parts, we have

$$\frac{t}{10} = \frac{11}{13}, \quad \text{or} \quad t = \frac{(11)(10)}{13} = 8 \text{ (nearly)}.$$

We add $t = 8$ to the last figure of 33.40 to obtain

$$N = \mathbf{33.48.} \quad Ans.$$

The essence of the process of interpolation is indicated in the foregoing procedure.   When the tabular difference is small, this process can easily be performed mentally.   However, the columns headed d and the proportional parts columns may be used in interpolation. Thus, to find t in the example just considered, we first find difference 11 as above, then read 13 in the column headed d to the right of the entry 5237, enter the proportional parts column headed 13, and since 11 is not listed, opposite the bold-faced **10** of this column read 8 in the column headed t.   Here there was a choice between **10** and 12.   We gave preference to the bold-faced entry.

The bold-facing in the proportional parts columns indicates the entry to be chosen whenever there is a choice.   Thus if we enter the proportional parts column headed 21 on p. 157 to find the value of t that corresponds to 7, we find there is a choice between the two partly bold-faced entries 6 and 8.   We choose 6, as the bold-faced part of 6 is nearer to 7.

52. EXPLANATION OF TABLE II

Tables of natural trigonometric functions.   In looking up the function of an angle between 0° and 45°, the value of the function will be found in the row (same horizontal line) with the angle and in the column headed by the name of the function.   If the angle is between 45° and 90°, the value of the function will be in the column with the name of the function at the bottom.

If the angle is not given exactly in the table, the value of the function can be found by interpolation. For example, to find sin 57° 24′, we take from the table the values in the following form and then compute the differences exhibited.

$$\left.\begin{array}{l} \sin 57° \ 00′ \\ \sin 57° \ 24′ \end{array}\right\} 24′ \left.\begin{array}{l} \\ 60′ = x \\ \end{array}\right. \left.\begin{array}{l} = 0.839 \\ \\ = 0.848 \end{array}\right\} y \left.\right\} 9$$

By the principle of proportional parts (§51), we have

$$\frac{24}{60} = \frac{y}{9}, \quad \text{or} \quad y = (9)\frac{24}{60} = 4 \text{ (nearly).}$$

We add $y = 4$ to the last two figures of 0.839 to obtain

$$\sin 57° \ 24′ = 0.843.$$

When the value of the function is given, the angle can be found by reversing the foregoing process.

53. EXPLANATION OF TABLE III

Table of logarithms of trigonometric functions. This table gives the four-place logarithms of sines, cosines, tangents, cotangents, secants, and cosecants for angles at intervals of 1°. Interpolation is necessary when the angle is given in degrees and minutes.

To find the logarithm when the angle is given. The following explanation shows how to find the logarithm of a trigonometric function when the angle is given.

Example. Find log sin 35° 15′.

Solution. From the table we find the logarithms in the following form and then compute the differences exhibited.

$$\left.\begin{array}{l} \log \sin 35° \ 0′ \\ \log \sin 35° \ 15′ \end{array}\right\} 15′ \left.\begin{array}{l} \\ 60′ = x \\ \end{array}\right. \left.\begin{array}{l} = 9.7586 - 10 \\ \\ = 9.7692 - 10 \end{array}\right\} y \left.\right\} d = 106$$

Then

$$\frac{y}{106} = \frac{15}{60}, \quad \text{or} \quad y = (106)\frac{15}{60} = 26 \text{ (nearly).}$$

∴ log sin 35° 15′ = 9.7586 − 10 + 0.0026 = 9.7612 − 10.

To find the angle when the logarithm is given. The following explanation shows how to find the angle when the logarithm of a trigonometric function is given.

Example. Find the acute angle B when log tan $B = 0.1492$.

Solution. From the table we find the logarithms in the following form and then compute the differences exhibited.

$$\begin{array}{l} \log \tan 54^\circ \\ \log \tan B \\ \log \tan 55^\circ \end{array} \left. \begin{array}{l} \\ \end{array} \right\} y \left. \begin{array}{l} \\ \\ \end{array} \right\} 60' \begin{array}{l} = 0.1387 \\ = 0.1492 \\ = 0.1548 \end{array} \left. \begin{array}{l} \\ \end{array} \right\} 105 \left. \begin{array}{l} \\ \\ \end{array} \right\} d = 161$$

$$\frac{y}{60} = \frac{105}{161}, \quad \text{or} \quad y = (60)\frac{105}{161} = 39' \text{ (nearly)}.$$

$$\therefore B = 54^\circ \ 39'.$$

FOUR-PLACE LOGARITHMIC

AND

TRIGONOMETRIC TABLES

TABLE I

COMMON LOGARITHMS

N	0	d	1	d	2	d	3	d	4	d	5	d	6	d	7	d	8	d	9	d
10	0000	43	0043	43	0086	42	0128	42	0170	42	0212	41	0253	41	0294	40	0334	40	0374	40
11	414	39	453	39	492	39	531	38	569	38	607	38	0645	37	0682	37	0719	36	0755	37
12	0792	36	0828	36	0864	35	0899	35	0934	35	0969	35	1004	34	1038	34	1072	34	1106	33
13	1139	34	1173	33	1206	33	1239	32	1271	32	1303	32	335	32	367	32	399	31	430	31
14	461	31	492	31	523	30	553	31	584	30	614	30	644	29	673	30	703	29	1732	29
15	1761	29	1790	28	1818	29	1847	28	1875	28	1903	28	1931	28	1959	28	1987	27	2014	27
16	2041	27	2068	27	2095	27	2122	26	2148	27	2175	26	2201	26	2227	26	2253	26	279	25
17	304	26	330	25	355	25	380	25	405	25	430	25	455	25	480	24	504	25	529	24
18	553	24	577	24	601	24	625	23	648	24	672	23	695	23	718	24	742	23	765	23
19	2788	22	2810	23	2833	23	2856	22	2878	22	2900	23	2923	22	2945	22	2967	22	2989	21
20	3010	22	3032	22	3054	21	3075	21	3096	22	3118	21	3139	21	3160	21	3181	20	3201	21
21	222	21	243	20	263	21	284	20	304	20	324	21	345	20	365	20	385	19	404	20
22	424	20	444	20	464	19	483	19	502	20	522	19	541	19	560	19	579	19	598	19
23	617	19	636	19	655	19	674	18	692	19	711	18	729	18	747	19	766	18	784	18
24	802	18	820	18	3838	18	3856	18	3874	18	3892	17	3909	18	3927	18	3945	17	3962	17
25	3979	18	3997	17	4014	17	4031	17	4048	17	4065	17	4082	17	4099	17	4116	17	4133	17
26	4150	16	4166	17	183	17	200	16	216	16	232	17	249	16	265	16	281	17	298	16
27	314	16	330	16	346	16	362	16	378	15	393	16	409	16	425	15	440	16	456	16
28	472	15	487	15	502	16	518	15	533	15	548	16	564	15	579	15	594	15	609	15
29	624	15	639	15	654	15	669	14	683	15	698	15	713	15	728	14	742	15	757	14
30	771	15	786	14	800	14	814	15	829	14	843	14	857	14	4871	15	4886	14	4900	14
31	4914	14	4928	14	4942	13	4955	14	4969	14	4983	14	4997	14	5011	13	5024	14	5038	13
32	5051	14	5065	14	5079	13	5092	13	5105	14	5119	13	5132	13	145	14	159	13	172	13
33	185	13	198	13	211	13	224	13	237	13	250	13	263	13	276	13	289	13	302	13
34	315	13	328	12	340	13	353	13	366	12	378	13	391	12	403	13	416	12	428	13
35	441	12	453	12	465	13	478	12	490	12	502	12	514	13	527	12	539	12	551	12
36	563	12	575	12	587	12	599	12	611	12	623	12	635	12	647	11	658	12	670	12
37	682	12	694	11	705	12	717	12	729	11	740	12	752	11	763	12	775	11	786	12
38	798	11	809	12	821	11	832	11	843	12	855	11	866	11	877	11	888	11	5899	12
39	5911	11	5922	11	5933	11	5944	11	5955	11	5966	11	5977	11	5988	11	5999	11	6010	11
40	6021	10	6031	11	6042	11	6053	11	6064	11	6075	10	6085	11	6096	11	6107	10	117	11
41	128	10	138	11	149	11	160	10	170	10	180	11	191	10	201	11	212	10	222	10
42	232	11	243	10	253	10	263	11	274	10	284	10	294	10	304	10	314	11	325	10
43	335	10	345	10	355	10	365	10	375	10	385	10	395	10	405	10	415	10	425	10
44	435	9	444	10	454	10	464	10	474	10	484	9	493	10	503	10	513	9	522	10
45	532	10	542	9	551	10	561	10	571	9	580	10	590	9	599	10	609	9	618	10
46	628	9	637	9	646	10	656	9	665	10	675	9	684	9	693	9	702	10	712	9
47	721	9	730	9	739	10	749	9	758	9	767	9	776	9	785	9	794	9	803	9
48	812	9	821	9	830	9	839	9	848	9	857	9	866	9	875	9	884	9	893	9
49	902	9	911	9	6920	9	6928	9	6937	9	6946	9	6955	9	6964	9	6972	9	6981	9
50	6990	8	6998	9	7007	9	7016	8	7024	9	7033	9	7042	8	7050	9	7059	8	7067	9
51	7076	8	7084	9	093	8	101	9	110	8	118	9	126	9	135	8	143	9	152	8
52	160	8	168	9	177	8	185	8	193	9	202	8	210	8	218	8	226	9	235	8
53	243	8	251	8	259	8	267	8	275	9	284	8	292	8	300	8	308	8	316	8
54	7324	8	7332	8	7340	8	7348	8	7356	8	7364	8	7372	8	7380	8	7388	8	7396	8
N	0		1		2		3		4		5		6		7		8		9	

t	43	42	41	40	39	38	37	36	35	34	33	32	31	30	29	28	27	26	25	24	t
								Proportional Parts													
0	0	0	0	0	0	0	0	0	0	0	0	0	0	0	0	0	0	0	0	0	0
1	4	4	4	4	4	4	4	4	4	3	3	3	3	3	3	3	3	3	3	2	1
2	9	8	8	8	8	8	7	7	7	7	7	6	6	6	6	6	5	5	5	5	2
3	13	13	12	12	12	11	11	11	10	10	10	10	9	9	9	8	8	8	8	7	3
4	17	17	16	16	16	15	15	14	14	14	13	13	12	12	12	11	11	10	10	10	4
5	22	21	20	20	20	19	18	18	18	17	16	16	16	15	14	14	14	13	12	12	5
6	26	25	25	24	23	23	22	22	21	20	20	19	19	18	17	17	16	16	15	14	6
7	30	29	29	28	27	27	26	25	24	24	23	22	22	21	20	20	19	18	18	17	7
8	34	34	33	32	31	30	30	29	28	27	26	26	25	24	23	22	22	21	20	19	8
9	39	38	37	36	35	34	33	32	32	31	30	29	28	27	26	25	24	23	22	22	9
10	43	42	41	40	39	38	37	36	35	34	33	32	31	30	29	28	27	26	25	24	10

TABLE I   COMMON LOGARITHMS

N	0	d	1	d	2	d	3	d	4	d	5	d	6	d	7	d	8	d	9	d
55	7404	8	7412	7	7419	8	7427	8	7435	8	7443	8	7451	8	7459	7	7466	8	7474	8
56	482	8	490	7	497	8	505	8	513	7	520	8	528	8	536	7	543	8	551	8
57	559	7	566	8	574	8	582	7	589	8	597	7	604	8	612	7	619	8	627	7
58	634	8	642	7	649	8	657	7	664	8	672	7	679	7	686	8	694	7	701	8
59	709	7	716	7	723	8	731	7	738	7	745	7	752	8	760	7	767	7	774	8
60	782	7	789	7	796	7	803	7	810	8	818	7	825	7	832	7	839	7	846	7
61	853	7	860	8	868	7	875	7	882	7	889	7	896	7	903	7	910	7	917	7
62	924	7	7931	7	7938	7	7945	7	7952	7	7959	7	7966	7	7973	7	7980	7	7987	6
63	7993	7	8000	7	8007	7	8014	7	8021	7	8028	7	8035	6	8041	7	8048	7	8055	7
64	8062	7	069	6	075	7	082	7	089	7	096	6	102	7	109	7	116	6	122	7
65	129	7	136	6	142	7	149	7	156	6	162	7	169	7	176	6	182	7	189	6
66	195	7	202	7	209	6	215	7	222	6	228	7	235	6	241	7	248	6	254	7
67	261	6	267	7	274	6	280	7	287	6	293	6	299	7	306	6	312	7	319	6
68	325	6	331	7	338	6	344	7	351	6	357	6	363	7	370	6	376	6	382	6
69	388	7	395	6	401	6	407	7	414	6	420	6	426	6	432	7	439	6	445	6
70	451	6	457	6	463	7	470	6	476	6	482	6	488	6	494	6	500	6	506	7
71	513	6	8519	6	8525	6	8531	6	8537	6	8543	6	8549	6	8555	6	8561	6	8567	6
72	8573	6	579	6	585	6	591	6	597	6	603	6	609	6	615	6	621	6	627	6
73	633	6	639	6	645	6	651	6	657	6	663	6	669	6	675	6	681	5	686	6
74	692	6	698	6	704	6	710	6	716	6	722	5	727	6	733	6	739	6	745	6
75	751	5	756	6	762	6	768	6	774	5	779	6	785	6	791	6	797	5	802	6
76	808	6	814	6	820	5	825	6	831	6	837	5	842	6	848	6	854	5	859	6
77	865	6	871	5	876	6	882	5	887	6	893	6	899	5	904	6	910	5	915	6
78	921	6	927	5	932	6	938	5	943	6	8949	5	8954	6	8960	5	8965	6	8971	5
79	8976	6	8982	5	8987	6	8993	5	8998	6	9004	5	9009	6	9015	5	9020	5	9025	6
80	9031	5	9036	6	9042	5	9047	6	9053	5	058	5	063	6	069	5	074	5	079	6
81	085	5	090	6	096	5	101	5	106	6	112	5	117	5	122	6	128	5	133	5
82	138	5	143	6	149	5	154	5	159	6	165	5	170	5	175	5	180	6	186	5
83	191	5	196	5	201	5	206	6	212	5	217	5	222	5	227	5	232	6	238	5
84	243	5	248	5	253	5	258	5	263	6	269	5	274	5	279	5	284	5	289	5
85	294	5	299	5	304	5	309	6	315	5	320	5	325	5	330	5	335	5	340	5
86	345	5	350	5	355	5	360	5	365	5	370	5	375	5	380	5	385	5	390	5
87	395	5	400	5	405	5	410	5	415	5	420	5	425	5	430	5	435	5	440	5
88	445	5	450	5	455	5	460	5	465	4	469	5	474	5	479	5	484	5	489	5
89	494	5	499	5	504	5	509	4	513	5	518	5	523	5	528	5	533	5	538	4
90	9542	5	9547	5	9552	5	9557	5	9562	4	9566	5	9571	5	9576	5	9581	5	9586	4
91	590	5	595	5	600	5	605	4	609	5	614	5	619	5	624	4	628	5	633	5
92	638	5	643	4	647	5	652	5	657	4	661	5	666	5	671	4	675	5	680	5
93	685	4	689	5	694	5	699	4	703	5	708	5	713	4	717	5	722	5	727	4
94	731	5	736	5	741	4	745	5	750	4	754	5	759	4	763	5	768	5	773	4
95	777	5	782	4	786	5	791	4	795	5	800	5	805	4	809	5	814	4	818	5
96	823	4	827	5	832	4	836	5	841	4	845	5	850	4	854	5	859	4	863	5
97	868	4	872	5	877	4	881	5	886	4	890	4	894	5	899	4	903	5	908	4
98	912	5	917	4	921	5	926	4	930	4	934	5	939	4	943	5	948	4	952	4
99	9956	5	9961	4	9965	4	9969	5	9974	4	9978	5	9983	4	9987	4	9991	5	9996	
N	0		1		2		3		4		5		6		7		8		9	

Proportional Parts

t	23	22	21	20	19	18	17	16	15	14	13	12	11	10	9	8	7	6	5	4	t
0	0	0	0	0	0	0	0	0	0	0	0	0	0	0	0	0	0	0	0	0	0
1	2	2	2	2	2	2	2	2	2	1	1	1	1	1	1	1	1	1	0	0	1
2	5	4	4	4	4	4	3	3	3	3	3	2	2	2	2	2	1	1	1	1	2
3	7	7	6	6	6	5	5	5	5	4	4	4	3	3	3	2	2	2	2	1	3
4	9	9	8	8	8	7	7	6	6	6	5	5	4	4	4	3	3	2	2	2	4
5	12	11	10	10	10	9	8	8	8	7	6	6	6	5	4	4	4	3	2	2	5
6	14	13	13	12	11	11	10	10	9	8	8	7	7	6	5	5	4	4	3	2	6
7	16	15	15	14	13	13	12	11	10	10	9	8	8	7	6	6	5	4	4	3	7
8	18	18	17	16	15	14	14	13	12	11	10	10	9	8	7	6	6	5	4	3	8
9	21	20	19	18	17	16	15	14	14	13	12	11	10	9	8	7	6	5	4	4	9
10	23	22	21	20	19	18	17	16	15	14	13	12	11	10	9	8	7	6	5	4	10

TABLE II

NATURAL TRIGONOMETRIC FUNCTIONS

Degrees	Sine	Cosecant	Tangent	Cotangent	Cosine	Secant	
0	0.000	∞	0.000	∞	1.000	1.000	90
1	017	57.299	017	57.290	1.000	000	89
2	035	28.654	035	28.636	0.999	001	88
3	052	19.107	052	19.081	999	001	87
4	070	14.336	070	14.301	998	002	86
5	087	11.474	087	11.430	996	004	85
6	105	9.567	105	9.514	995	006	84
7	122	8.206	123	8.144	993	008	83
8	139	7.185	141	7.115	990	010	82
9	156	6.392	158	6.314	988	012	81
10	174	5.759	176	5.671	985	015	80
11	191	5.241	194	5.145	982	019	79
12	208	4.810	213	4.705	978	022	78
13	225	445	231	331	974	026	77
14	242	4.134	249	4.011	970	031	76
15	259	3.864	268	3.732	966	035	75
16	276	628	287	487	961	040	74
17	292	420	306	271	956	046	73
18	309	236	325	3.078	951	051	72
19	326	3.072	344	2.904	946	058	71
20	342	2.924	364	747	940	064	70
21	358	790	384	605	934	071	69
22	375	669	404	475	927	079	68
23	391	559	424	356	921	086	67
24	407	459	445	246	914	095	66
25	0.423	366	0.466	145	0.906	1.103	65
26	438	281	488	2.050	899	113	64
27	454	203	510	1.963	891	122	63
28	469	130	532	881	883	133	62
29	485	063	554	804	875	143	61
30	500	2.000	577	732	866	155	60
31	515	1.942	601	664	857	167	59
32	530	887	625	600	848	179	58
33	545	836	649	540	839	192	57
34	559	788	675	483	829	206	56
35	574	743	700	428	819	221	55
36	588	701	727	376	809	236	54
37	602	662	754	327	799	252	53
38	616	624	781	280	788	269	52
39	629	589	810	235	777	287	51
40	643	556	839	192	766	305	50
41	656	524	869	150	755	325	49
42	669	494	900	111	743	346	48
43	682	466	933	072	731	367	47
44	695	440	0.966	036	719	390	46
45	0.707	1.414	1.000	1.000	0.707	1.414	45
	Cosine	Secant	Cotangent	Tangent	Sine	Cosecant	Degrees

For explanation of this table see §52.

TABLE III
LOGARITHMS OF TRIGONOMETRIC FUNCTIONS

De-grees	l sin	l csc	l tan	l cot	l sec	l cos	De-grees
0	$-\infty$	∞	$-\infty$	∞	10.0000	10.0000	90
1	8.2419	11.7581	8.2419	11.7581	0001	9.9999	89
2	5428	4572	5431	4569	0003	9997	88
3	7188	2812	7194	2806	0006	9994	87
4	8436	1564	8446	1554	0011	9989	86
5	8.9403	11.0597	8.9420	11.0580	0017	9983	85
6	9.0192	10.9808	9.0216	10.9784	0024	9976	84
7	0859	9141	0891	9109	0032	9968	83
8	1436	8564	1478	8522	0042	9958	82
9	1943	8057	1997	8003	0054	9946	81
10	2397	7603	2463	7537	0066	9934	80
11	2806	7194	2887	7113	0081	9919	79
12	3179	6821	3275	6725	0096	9904	78
13	3521	6479	3634	6366	0113	9887	77
14	3837	6163	3968	6032	0131	9869	76
15	4130	5870	4281	5719	0151	9849	75
16	4403	5597	4575	5425	0172	9828	74
17	4659	5341	4853	5147	0194	9806	73
18	4900	5100	5118	4882	0218	9782	72
19	5126	4874	5370	4630	0243	9757	71
20	5341	4659	5611	4389	0270	9730	70
21	5543	4457	5842	4158	0298	9702	69
22	5736	4264	6064	3936	0328	9672	68
23	5919	4081	6279	3721	0360	9640	67
24	6093	3907	6486	3514	0393	9607	66
25	9.6259	10.3741	9.6687	10.3313	10.0427	9.9573	65
26	6418	3582	6882	3118	0463	9537	64
27	6570	3430	7072	2928	0501	9499	63
28	6716	3284	7257	2743	0541	9459	62
29	6856	3144	7438	2562	0582	9418	61
30	6990	3010	7614	2386	0625	9375	60
31	7118	2882	7788	2212	0669	9331	59
32	7242	2758	7958	2042	0716	9284	58
33	7361	2639	8125	1875	0764	9236	57
34	7476	2524	8290	1710	0814	9186	56
35	7586	2414	8452	1548	0866	9134	55
36	7692	2308	8613	1387	0920	9080	54
37	7795	2205	8771	1229	0977	9023	53
38	7893	2107	8928	1072	1035	8965	52
39	7989	2011	9084	0916	1095	8905	51
40	8081	1919	9238	0762	1157	8843	50
41	8169	1831	9392	0608	1222	8778	49
42	8255	1745	9544	0456	1289	8711	48
43	8338	1662	9697	0303	1359	8641	47
44	8418	1582	9.9848	0152	1431	8569	46
45	9.8495	10.1505	10.0000	10.0000	10.1505	9.8495	45
	l cos	l sec	l cot	l tan	l csc	l sin	De-grees

Note. Each logarithm in this table is to have -10 written after it. For explanation of this table see §53.

ANSWERS

§3.   Pages 6 to 8.

1. 1700 sq. in.
2. 12.566 sq. in.
3. 10 ft. by 20 ft.
4. (a) $\sqrt{2}a$,
   (b) $\sqrt{b^2 + h^2}$
5. $\frac{1}{4}\sqrt{3}a^2$.
6. $\frac{1}{4}\pi d^2$.
7. $C = \pi d$.

8. 7200 sq. ft.,
   84.852 ft.
9. 0.58905 sq. in.
10. 53,046 sq. ft.,
   622.70 ft., 264.16 ft.
11. 13.3 sq. ft.
12. 136.48 sq. ft.
13. 10.155 ft.
14. 51.228 sq. in.

15. 51.132 sq. in.
16. 1120 ft.
17. 107,070 sq. ft.,
   180.52 yd.
18. $\frac{1}{3}\pi(7 + 4\sqrt{3})a^2$,
   107.12.
19. 4.8 in.
20. 30.57.

§5.   Page 14.

10. (a) 2.5 ft.,
   (b) $2.5\sqrt{3}$ ft.,

   (c) $2.5\sqrt{2}$ ft.,
   (d) 3.993 ft.,

   (e) 3.701 ft.
12. $16\frac{2}{3}$ ft.

General Exercises.   Page 17.

10. 24 ft.

§9.   Pages 20, 21.

1. $\sqrt{3}a$.
2. 375 cu. in.
3. 10.079 ft.
5. 460 lb.
6. 3.3528 cu. ft.
   13.441 sq. ft.
7. 122.91 sq. ft.

8. A 6.
   B 8, 12, 6, 1.
   C 27.
   D 3.
   E 1, 3, 3, 1, 8.
9. $\frac{1}{2}\sqrt{5}a^2$.
10. $\frac{1}{2}\sqrt{2}a^2$.

11. $\dfrac{\sqrt{3}}{9}$.
12. $\dfrac{\sqrt{6}}{36}$.
13. $3\sqrt{3}$.
14. 63° 26′.

§10.   Pages 24, 25.

1. 27 tons.
2. $192.
3. 72,576 bricks.
4. 99.66 sq. ft.
5. 206.22 cu. **yd.**
6. 3453.9 lb.
   7983.6 lb.
7 Second is twice as
   large as first.

8. 13.424 cu. ft.
9 120.46 cu. ft.
10. A   6.
   B (a) 8.
      (b) 12.
      (c) 4.
      (d) 0.
   C   24.
11. $\sqrt{a^2 + b^2 + c^2}$.

12. $4\sqrt{10}$, 3.5, 8.72.
13. (a) 33° 41′, 36° 42′,
      35° 23′, 53° 18′,
      68° 59′, 24° 50′.
   (b) 50, 83.895, 97.628.
   (c) 7.6823 in.
14. 21° 48′, 47° 58′,
   33° 51′.

161

§12. Page 28.

1. ha^2.

2. $2a^2b$.

3. $225\sqrt{3} = 389.71$ cu. ft.

4. $\pi a^2 h$.

§13. Pages 30 to 32.

1. $T = S + 2B$.

2. (a) $V = a^2h$,
(b) $T = 2a^2 + 4ah$.

3. $\frac{3}{4}\sqrt{3} = 1.2990$ cu. in.

5. 80 sq. ft.

6. 2.1134 in.

7. 440 cu. yd.

8. 5.1235 in.

9. $3000.

10. (a) 6000 cu. ft.,
(b) 16,136 blocks.

11. 4800 cu. yd.

12. $13,396.

13. 4880 cu. yd.

14. (a) 22.857 gal.
(b) 8.9286 gal.
(c) 5.7966 in.
(d) 801 sq. in.

15. 141,720 cu. ft.

16. 24,709 cu. ft.

§15. Pages 35, 36.

1. 24.834 sq. ft.

3. 67,881 gal.

4. 4356 tons.

5. 26,136,000 cu. ft.

6. 125 cu. yd.

7. 691.2 cu. ft.

8 38 cu. in.

9. 21.206 cu. in.

10. (a) 178.13 cu. ft.
(b) 247.40 cu. ft.
(c) 211.11 cu. ft.
(d) 100.20 cu. ft.

11. 840 cu. ft.

§16. Pages 38, 39.

1. 0.57596 gal.
3273.4 lb.

2. 0.45815 cu. ft.
21.991 sq. ft.

3. 103,690 cu. ft.

4. 157.08 cu. ft.
353.43 sq. ft.

5. 33,695 cu. ft.

6. 18.946 lb.

7. 4.699 cu. ft.

§17. Pages 41, 42.

1. 1480.4 gal.

2. 1.3617 ft.

3. 139.06 cu. in.

4. 8.5704 in.
380.79 sq. in.

5. 164.94 cu. in.

6. 4740.4 sq. ft.

7. 15.316 cents.

8. 36.912 lb.

9. 1.5910 by 1.5910 by 15 ft.

10. 30.790 by 61.580 ft.

11. 113,100 cu. cm.

12. 3859.5 cu. in.

13. 41.887 cu. in.,
109.32 sq. in.

14. (a) 452.39 cu. in.
(b) 339.29 cu. in.

15. 47.124 cu. ft.

16. 59.341 cu. in.
121.54 sq. in.

§18. Pages 42 to 45.

1. $533\frac{1}{3}$ cu. yd.

2. 376.01 cu. in.

3. 97.778 cu. yd.

4. $\frac{77}{48} = 1.6041$ ft.

5. 0.95245.

6. 128.76 cu. in.

7. 509.30 ft.

8. 216,000.

9. 800 bu.

10. 5184.

11. 50.471.

12. 236.56 lb.

13. 1986.

14. 4.8700 in. $\times$ 9.7400 in.

15. 8 sq. in.; 3.4642 in. from original section.

16. 0.1337 in.
17. 109.60 cu. in.
319.86 sq. in.
18. 369.08 cu. in.
320.95 sq. in.
19. 1160.76 cu. in.
811.84 sq. in.
20. (a) 9 in.
(b) 92° 59'.
(c) 38.418 sq. in.
(d) 20° 26'.
21. 20.944 cu. in.

22. (a) $AC = BG = AF = 14.142$;
$AH = EB = 11.662$; $EG = 14.697$.
(b) Angle $AEF =$ angle $DHG = 111°$ 48'.
Angle $BFE =$ angle $CGH = 68°$ 12'. All others 90°.

(c) $FD = AG = 17.320$ in.
(d) 320 sq. in.
(e) 527.7 sq. in.
(f) 74° 12'.
(g) 800 cu. in.
23. 28,752 cu. ft.
24. 9° 43', 30° 28', 57° 32'.
25. 36° 52'.
26. (a) 4° 29', (b) 9° 50'.

§20. Pages 49, 50.

1. $\frac{1}{3}Bh$.
2. $6\frac{2}{3}$ tons.
3. 1199.0 lb.

4. 29,531 cu. in.
5. 5.5556 ft.
6. 334.82 sq. in.

8. 29°4', 53°8', 58°22'.
172 sq. in.
9. 39,100 cu. ft.

§21. Pages 52, 53.

1. 204.8 bu.
2. $44.19.
3. 307,600 lb.
4. $34,901,000.

5. 686.53 sq. ft.
6. Regular tetrahedron.
7. 25,798 sq. ft.
392,150 cu. ft.

8. 128 sq. in.
9. $\frac{1}{12}\sqrt{2}a^3$.
11. 45°.

§22. Page 56.

1. 1728 times as large.
2. $\dfrac{V_E}{V_M} = \dfrac{(198)^3}{(54)^3}$.
3. $\dfrac{S_1}{S_2} = \dfrac{1}{4}$.
4. Edge = 1.5874 ft.

5. 4 ft., 6 ft., 8 ft.
6. $r = 2.5198$ ft.
$h = 3.7797$ ft.
7. 0.45013 cu. ft.
8. 160-lb. man.
9. 240 lb.
10. 287.44 gal.

11. 0.35355.
12. 3.1748 ft.
13. 1269.9 sq. in.
14. No. The 790-ft. vessel.
15. No.

§24. Page 59.

1. 16.219×10^8 cu. yd.
2. 308.66 lb.
3. 13.5 sq. ft.

4. 452.39 cu. in.
5. $\frac{1}{6}\pi a^2 h(3 - 2\sqrt{2})$.

6. $\frac{1}{2}\sqrt{2}h, \dfrac{h}{\sqrt[3]{2}}$.

8. arc tan $\dfrac{a}{h}$, arc tan $\dfrac{a}{h}$, 2 arc sin $\dfrac{a\sqrt{2}}{2\sqrt{a^2 + h^2}}$.

§25. Pages 63, 64.

1. 453,900 lb.
2. 61.061 sq. yd.
3. 1197.0 sq. ft.
4. 5.1510 ft.
5. $\dfrac{\pi\sqrt{3}R^3}{24}$.

6. (a) $V = \dfrac{7\pi d^2 h}{24}$.
(b) 92.548 cu. in.
7. 8.3980 in.
8. 144°.

9. (a) 49.562 cu. in.
(b) 109.51 cu. in.
(c) 391.78 cu. in.
(d) 673.26 cu. in.
(e) 664.82 cu. in.
10. 60° 30', 47° 56'.

§26. Pages 64 to 66.

1. $132.00.
2. 226.19.
3. 6.3496, 4.7622, 3.1748.
4. 326.06 sq. ft.
5. 21,942 long tons.
6. $\dfrac{A_s}{A_P} = \dfrac{16}{9}.$
7. $\dfrac{\sqrt{2}}{2}\,h = 0.70710h.$
(h = height of tent)

8. 942.48 cu. ft.
9. (a) 3780 lb.
(b) 133,110.
10. 3,700,000 lb.
11. 8 cu. in.
12. 117.29 cu. in.
13. 305.69 cu. yd.
14. (a) 1.6108 in.
(b) 113.57 sq. in.
15. 15.708 cu. ft.
17. $\frac{1}{6}$.
18. $\frac{1}{6}$.

19. $\frac{1}{8}$.
20. $\sqrt[3]{\frac{1}{3}}h,\ \sqrt[3]{\frac{2}{3}}h.$
21. $\dfrac{2xh}{2h + \sqrt{x^2 + h^2}}.$
22. $\sqrt{\dfrac{x^3}{x + \sqrt{x^2 + h^2}}}.$
23. 259.60 sq. in.
24. $\frac{1}{3}a^3,\ (2 + \sqrt{2})a^2.$
25. 384 cu. in.
26. 1.38 in.

§28. Pages 70, 71.

1. $\dfrac{64.9}{67.2}.$
2. 0.60484 ft.
3. 353,440 lb.

4. 2426.7 cu. yd.
5. $102\frac{1}{8}$ cu. in.
6. 348.78 sq. ft.

7. $1\frac{17}{25}$.
8. 1098.0 cu. ft.
9. 101.17 cu. ft.

§29. Pages 74, 75.

2. $20.95.
3. 508.78 cu. in.
4. 221.66 sq. in.
5. 39.603 pt.
6. $131.95.

7. 934.62 cu. ft.
762.58 sq. ft.
8. 29,985 sq. ft.
9. 997.08 lb.
10. 0.26319h.
11. $\frac{7}{19}$.

12. 339.29 sq. ft., 571.77 sq. ft., 8.7750 ft., 21.938 ft., 1001.6 cu. ft.
13. 55° 9′.

§30. Pages 78 to 80.

1. 148,741 cu. yd.
2. 5648.7 cu. yd.
3. 1212 cu. ft.
4. 24 ft.

5. 31,111 cu. yd.
6. 23,760 short tons.
7. $858.33.
8. $695.24.

10. $1080.
11. 53.5 cu. ft.
12. 366 cu. ft.

§31. Pages 82, 83.

1. 1103.0.
2. 10.472 cu. in.

4. (a) 188 sq. in.
(b) 240 sq. in.
(c) 192 cu. in.

(d) 81° 52′.
(e) 51° 24′.
(f) 40 sq. in.

§32. Pages 83 to 86.

1. 716.28 cu. meters.
2. $43.64.
3. 2412 cu. ft.
4. 39,172 cu. yd.
5. 1255 short tons.

6. (a) 1521.3 sq. ft.
(b) 259.15 sq. ft.
7. $31.94.
8. 1.2726 cu. ft.
9. 196 sq. ft.

10. 86,068 cu. ft.
11. 27,556 cu. yd.
12. 607.5 cu. ft., 494.02 sq. ft.
13. 310 cu. ft.

14. 12 ft.
15. 16.9 ft.
16. 33.6 ft.
17. 13 cu. in.
18. $\frac{1}{3}h$ cu. ft., where h is the common altitude.

19. $\frac{1}{3}Bh$.
20. $26\frac{1}{3}$.
21. (a) 40π sq. in.
(b) 271.00 sq. in.
23. (a) $18\sqrt{2}$ sq. in.
(b) $2\sqrt{22}$ sq. in.

(c) $9\sqrt{5}$ sq. in.
(d) $12\sqrt{3}$ sq. in.
(e) $9\sqrt{5}$ sq. in.
24. (a) 203 cu. ft.
(b) 28° 4′.
(c) 126 sq. ft.

§33. Pages 92, 93.

2. 1005.3 lb.
3. 549 lb.
4. \$43,971.
5. 539.74 lb.
6. 5026.6 sq. ft.
33,510 cu. ft.
7. 1818.1 lb.
8. 1.9906×10^8 sq. mi.
2.6408×10^{11} cu. mi.

9. 24,798 lb.
312.68 cu. in.
10. 18 cents.
11. $(3\sqrt{2} + 2)r$.
12. 319.89 cu. in.,
226.19 sq. in.
13. 24.056 cu. in.
14. $\dfrac{V_i}{V_c} = \dfrac{1}{3\sqrt{3}}$.

15. 1.9109 cu. in.
16. 362.33 cu. in.
17. 471 sq. in.,
962 cu. in.
20. 0.51548 cu. in.
21. $[1 - \pi(\frac{5}{4} - \frac{2}{3}\sqrt{2})]a^3$.

§35. Pages 96, 97.

3. 7.97×10^7 sq. mi.
4. 15.708 sq. ft.
5. 263.89 sq. in.
6. 0.8579 in.
7. 328 sq. in.

8. $\dfrac{2\pi r^2 h}{r + h}$
104.72 sq. ft.
9. 0.1830 of its area.

10. $\frac{1}{3}$ of it.
11. 142.80 sq. mi.
12. 132.60 sq. ft.
14. 123 sq. in.

§36. Pages 101, 102.

3. 37.062 pt.
4. 84.823 cu. in.
73.304 cu. in.
5. 51.852 per cent.

6. 2 in.
7. 34,050 cu. in.
8. 0.762 in.

9. $\dfrac{5\pi R^3}{12}$.
12. 10.243 in.

§37. Page 106.

1. \$1.1694.
2. 6545.0 cu. in.

3. 2654.7 cu. in.
4. 1.5 cu. in.

5. 156.25 lb.
6. \$1.47.

§38. Pages 107 to 109.

1. 1.0019×10^{10} cu. mi.
2. \$11.31.
3. 291.07 lb.
4. 58.74 per cent.
5. (a) 94.638 sq. in.
(b) 71.210 cu. in.
6. $80\pi = 251.33$ sq. in.

7. 6.1545 mi.
8. R (radius of earth).
9. 120.48 cu. in.
10. 0.78860 lb.
11. 325.07 cu. ft.
12. 10.243 in.
13. 300.05 sq. in.,
558.38 cu. in.

15. (a) $\dfrac{5\pi R^3}{24}$.
(b) $\dfrac{3\pi R^3}{8}$.
16. $0.4764\ R^3$.
17. 502.65 cu. in.
18. Radius $= \frac{9}{32}(3\sqrt{2} - 2\sqrt{3})$.

19. (a) $\dfrac{1 + \sqrt{2}}{4}$.

(b) $\frac{1}{4}$.

20. 2.306 in.

21. (a) 90°.   (b) $\frac{8}{3}\pi R^3$.
(c) πR^3.   (d) $\frac{5}{3}\pi R^3$.
(e) $\frac{1}{3}\pi R^3$.

22. (a) 67.021, 25.133,
41.887, 8.3776.
(b) 431.26, 161.72,
269.54, 53.908.

23. $0.70475 R^2$.

24. $V = \dfrac{4}{3}\,\pi \left(\dfrac{r}{h}\right)^3 \times$
$(\sqrt{r^2 + h^2} - r)^3$

25. (a) $\dfrac{S_c}{S_s} = \dfrac{1}{2}$.

(b) $\dfrac{V_s}{V_c} = \dfrac{4\sqrt{2}}{3}$.

26. (a) 450 cu. in.
(b) 535 cu. in.
(c) 585 cu. in.
(d) 636 cu. in.

27. 89 cu. in.

29. $\dfrac{V_s}{V_T} = \dfrac{\pi\sqrt{3}}{18}$.

30. (a) $5 + \sqrt{7}$.
(b) $3(2 + \sqrt{2})$.

31. $3.0861R$, $4.3644R$.

32. (a) $\frac{1}{2}\pi R^2$.
(b) $\frac{1}{4}\pi R^2$.
(c) $\frac{1}{2}[3\,(\text{arc}\tan \frac{1}{2}\sqrt{2})$
$+ \sqrt{2}]\,R^2$.

33. 2° 23′.

§40.   Pages 114, 115.

1. 2301.0 cu. in.

2. 197.39 cu. ft.

3. 1105.4 cu. in.
1174.5 sq. in.

4. 667.58 lb.

5. 444.13 cu. in.

6. 5211.1 cu. in.

7. 5790.1 cu. ft.

8. $\dfrac{4r}{3\pi}$ distant from each
bounding radius.

9. $\dfrac{2r}{\pi}$ distant from each
radius through an
end.

10. 1 ft.

11. $\dfrac{2r}{\pi}\,(2 - \sqrt{3})$ distant
from one bound-
ing radius, $\dfrac{2r}{\pi}$ distant from a line
through the cen-
ter of the circle
and perpendicu-
lar to the same
bounding radius.

12. $\dfrac{h(2a + b)}{3(a + b)}$ distant
from base b,
$\dfrac{a^2 + b^2 + ab}{3(a + b)}$ distant from side h.

14. $\dfrac{3r}{\pi}$ distant from center of circle along
the radius bisect-
ing the arc.

15. (a) $19\pi a^2$.
(b) $\dfrac{19\pi a^3}{3}$.

16. (a) $\frac{2}{3}$.   (b) $\frac{4}{5}$.

17. $\frac{1}{12}\pi(9\sqrt{3} - 4\pi)R^3$.

§41.   Pages 118, 119.

4. 1.7 in.

6. $\dfrac{T_D}{T_I} = \dfrac{\sqrt{9} + 3\sqrt{5}}{\sqrt{5} - \sqrt{5}}$,
$\dfrac{V_D}{V_I} = \dfrac{3}{10}(5 + 3\sqrt{5})$.

7. 1043.

10. 625 lb.

11. 70° 32′.

12. 3.

13. 250.32 sq. in., 256
cu. in.

§42.   Page 121.

3. $A_y = bc - [2bc - a(b + c)]\dfrac{y}{h} + (b - a)\,(c - a)\dfrac{y^2}{h^2}$, where a is an edge of
the square and b, c sides of the rectangle.

4. $A_y = a^2 + a(b + c - a)\dfrac{y}{h} + [\frac{1}{2}bc - a(b + c)]\dfrac{y^2}{h^2}$, where a is the side of
square and b, c are legs of the right triangle.

§44. Pages 125 to 129.

1. (a) 32, (b) $76\frac{1}{2}$.
2. $\frac{4}{3}\pi R^3$.
3. $\frac{1}{3}\pi h^2(3R - h)$.
4. $\frac{1}{6}\pi h(3b^2 + h^2)$.
5. $\frac{1}{6}\pi h(3a^2 + 3b^2 + h^2)$.
6. $\frac{1}{3}\pi h(r^2 + R^2 + Rr)$.
7. $\frac{1}{2}\pi bh^2$.
9. $\frac{4}{3}\pi abc$.
10. $\frac{1}{3}\pi abh$.
11. $\frac{1}{6}h(B + 4M)$.
12. $\frac{2}{3}h(B + 2M)$.
13. $5\frac{1}{3}$ cu. ft.
14. $83\frac{1}{3}$ cu. in.

15. (a) 18,475 cu. in.
    (b) 10,667 cu. in.
    (c) 21,333 cu. in.
    (d) 21,333 cu. in.
    (e) 42,667 cu. in.
16. $533\frac{1}{3}$ cu. in.
17. (a) $\frac{16}{3}r^3$.
    (b) $\frac{8}{3}r^3$, when a leg is in the plane of the circle; $\frac{4}{3}r^3$, when the hypotenuse is in the plane of the circle.

18. 24π.
19. $\frac{1}{3}\pi R^3$.
20. $\frac{1}{2}\sqrt{3b^2h}$.
21. $2666\frac{2}{3}$ cu. in.
22. $\frac{8}{3}a^3$.
23. $\frac{16}{3}r^3$.
25. 2440 cu. ft.
26. $\frac{2}{3}\pi a^2h$.

§45. Page 130.

2. When $L = \dfrac{1}{4}\dfrac{b^2}{a}$. $\dfrac{1}{2}\dfrac{b}{a}$ below the lower base.

§47. Pages 133 to 143.

1. 99.266 lb.
2. 6.0241 ft.
3. $46\frac{2}{3}$ in.
4. 137.71 cu. ft.
5. 510 short tons.
6. 9.8960 sq. ft.
7. 55,004 ft.
8. 3.0286 in.
   3640 sq. ft.
9. $14\pi^2 = 138.18$ cu. in.
10. 1792 cu. in.
11. 9.1328 cu. ft.
12. 217 days.
13. 2689.2 cu. in.
14. 49,352 short tons.
15. 636.70 cu. in.
16. 37.529 sq. ft.
17. 12,408,000 gal.
18. 1300.7 cu. yd.
19. Cylindrical can.
20. 22,140 cu. ft.
21. 14.545 cu. ft.
22. 11.454 sq. ft.
23. 46.564 in.

24. No.
25. 56.312 hr.
26. 1.2599 ft.
27. 154.86 cu. ft.
28. 615.63 sq. ft.
29. 0.011295 cu. in.
30. 0.28274 cu. ft.
31. (a) $1083.20.
    (b) $231.90.
32. 11 cups.
33. 30-cent ones.
34. 6.9208 cu. in.
35. 1050.1 loads.
36. 255.52 cu. in.
37. 7840 cu. ft.
38. (a) 89.536 cu. ft.
    (b) 57 cu. ft.
    (c) 36 cu. ft.
    (d) 432 board ft.
39. 3518.6 bu.
40. Volume of prism is 3 times the volume of the other solid.
41. 534,380 lb.
42. 21.206 cu. in.

43. A 12.
    B (a) 8, (b) 36, (c) 54, (d) 27.
    C 125.
44. 11,084 cu. ft.
45. Rectangle; right triangle.
46. $4912.90.
47. 0.62280 cu. in.
48. 561,230 cu. yd.
49. 2 ft.
    3.4816 pt.
50. 494.96 lb.
51. 31.784 cu. in.
    60.216 sq. in.
52. 10 in.
    1040 lb.
53. 2620.8 lb.
54. 2059.2 lb.
    33 cu. ft.
    45 per cent.
55. 40.776 lb.
56. 2290.2 cu. in.
    114.51 lb.
57. 1,908.5 lb.

58. 1.5625 cu. in.
254.31 cu. ft.

59. 1.2991 cu. in.

60. 1995.5 bu.

61. 869.5 cu. ft.

62. 174,240,000 cu. ft.

63. height = 40 in., diameter = 30 in., thickness = 2.5 in.

64. 8 days.

65. 318 cu. ft.

66. 46.098 sq. in.

67. $\frac{1}{1008}$ in.

69. $\pi^2 a^3$.

70. 232 sq. in.

71. 10.079 in.

72. $\frac{4}{9}$.

73. 899.48 lb.

74. 1363 sq. in., 1840 cu. in.

75. 154.78 short tons.

76. 523.95 cu. in.
314.16 sq. in.

77. 48.36 cu. in., 188.50 sq. in.; 2875.8 cu. in., 942.48 sq. in.

78. (a) $3\pi R^2$, $\frac{9}{4}\pi R^2$, $4\pi R^2$. (b) $\frac{1}{2}\sqrt{2}\pi R^3$, $\frac{3}{8}\pi R^3$, $\frac{4}{3}\pi R^3$.

79. (a) $\frac{13}{24}\pi R^3$.
(b) $\frac{275}{24}\pi R^3$.
(c) $\frac{1}{4}\sqrt[3]{550}R$.

80. 104.06 sq. ft.

81. 73.592 sq. ft.

83. 569,200 cu. ft.

84. $\dfrac{Y}{Z} = \dfrac{14}{13}$.

85. (a) $\frac{2}{3}\pi r^3\left(1 - \dfrac{r}{\sqrt{r^2+R^2}}\right)$
(b) $7.2\pi = 22.620$.

86. $4 + 2\sqrt{2}$ in.

87. 4.5 cu. in.

88. 5.7 in., 25° 6'.

89. 37.028 sq. in.
10.204 cu. in.

90. 1.0087 in.

91. (a) 89 cu. ft.
(b) 75 cu. ft.

92. 4.76 in., 17° 48'.

93. 23° 35'.

94. 39.3 sq. in., 11.6 cu. in.

95. 8,150,000 sq. mi., where radius of earth = 3960 mi.

96. 25.73 cu. in.

97. 53° 8'.

99. 0.79 cm.

100. (a) 102° 38',
(b) 151 sq. in.,
(c) 402 cu. in.,
(d) 204 cu. in.,
(e) 198 cu. in.

102. 15° 35' or 143° 1'.

103. 6.16 cm.

104. $\frac{3}{2}\sqrt{208}$ ft.

INDEX